A Balanced Blend of Blues

Darren Gandy

ISBN: 978-1-945526-17-6

Library of Congress Control Number: 2017952799

Photos courtesy of Clark and Glynis Buschmann

Dedicated to my father, for his support and help with editing, and his father, Bruce Gandy Sr., for his brilliant contributions to mankind.

Acknowledgements

I would like to thank my Creator for giving me these talents, His Son for giving me peace, and His Spirit for giving me direction.

My sincere appreciation to my father and mother for instilling good traits, and being fine, loving parents, and to my Uncle A.J. and Aunt Emily for all of their support and love, especially during the last days that I spent in Marysville; I am truly grateful and lucky to have all of them in my life.

I would also like to take this opportunity to thank the wonderfully supportive staff at the Twin Cities Rescue Mission in Marysville. They are a key player in not only my recovery, but continue to be a shining light to the residents of Yuba and Sutter Counties here in California. You are a blessing!

My heartfelt gratitude goes out to: all of the Staff at CARES Community Health, Sacramento, for ALL of my health care; medical, dental, chiropractic, therapy, but most of all to the psychiatry department for their integral part in helping me learn to utilize my tools to achieve a fuller potential, and to Harm Reduction Services for their undying love, support, and a free monthly bus sticker. You rock!

I would like to take the opportunity to extend my deep gratitude to the owners and staff of North Side Recovery: Bill and Patty, Bill G, Bob, Nicole, Julia, Christie, Doc, Cappy, and Mr. Cool (the cat), and all the previous staff there. You saved my life.

I would like to thank the many wonderful teachers, mentors, and professionals that have helped me along my thick path.

Finally, grateful gratitude goes out to Gerry and the I Street Press for helping me realize my dream of being a published author. Thanks!

Prologue: Why are we here?

"Then I commended mirth, because a man hath no better thing under the sun, than to eat, and to drink, and to be merry: for that shall abide with him of his labour the days of his life, which God giveth him under the sun."
King Solomon; Ecclesiastes 8:15

Now, I am not going to claim that I have discovered the purpose for existence, BUT, I will say that, after experiencing a little over a half-century of life, I truly believe that I have gotten a glimpse of a reflection of the ice-berg that represents the purpose for MY existence. I am utilizing the age-old philosophical reference to the "ice berg" metaphor. It represents the fact that, when you "see" an ice berg floating, you are *only able* to visually observe a very small fraction of the whole; a lot remains invisible, or "beneath the surface", if you will.

"Hey-hey, my-my. Rock-and-roll will never die. There's more to the picture, than meets the eye. Hey-hey, my-my"
Neil Young

You see, there is always *so much more* to this age-old question. To give you an example, I am going to attempt to define a scenario of multi-layer meaning: if you saw me walking out of Wal-Mart with a bag, you could conclude that I had just conducted a professional interaction, wherein, I am a consumer, paying currency for goods, or a product. But, if you had been with me earlier that day, you would realize that I had just seen a documentary on "Heavenly Blue Morning Glory" flowers, and you would understand that I went to procure seeds, pots, growing medium, and an appropriate fertilizer.
If you go back just a few more years, my past would reveal a

fascination with botany, and photosynthesis, where plants use a chemical called chlorophyll and sunlight to symbiotically convert the carbon-dioxide that we exhale, back into oxygen.

Then you can go deeper even from there, if you care to delve into the tiny realm of the sub-atomic particles of electrons, protons, and neutrons; and deeper, and *deeper* . . . Wisdom, truth, and enlightenment are like hidden gleaming gems. I, through my writing, am attempting to shine my own personal light on those gorgeous, (and other-wise), facets that have been revealed to me in all states of consciousness and perceptions; both real and altered. I have formulated a number of postulates, or "tenets" of life. Here are three that I believe are appropriate:

1. You can only experience joy to the depth which you have felt sorrow,
2. There are many over-lapping cycles and layers,
3. The purpose for existence is to interact in a mutually beneficial manner.

David S Viscott, radio personality, once said, “The meaning of life is to find your gift. The work of life is to develop this gift. The purpose of life is to give it away”.

This means that, say, you are a car detailer, and I make furniture. I would build a chair with wheels for you to relax in while you detail my Ferrari. We not only work together, but we are also able to bring out the best of our personal abilities; and this becomes an inspiration to everyone who sees our teamwork!

It is my honor to share these writings with you, as a fellow sojourner, or "pilgrim" on this space-ship, planet earth. Here you will find evidence of goodness, recovery, and the realization that life is something to be shared, enjoyed, and treasured.

Thank-you for joining me in this exciting and exponentially expanding experience as we enjoy

~life~

in all of its fullness.

"The purpose for life IS life" Alan Alda, actor

Blessings,
Brother Badger

Table of Contents

A Balanced Blend of Blues

In memory of Janis Joplin, Jimi Hendrix, and Jim Morrison

To efficiently enact, and
perform the *blues*,
ya gotta' live those
turbulent hues

Traveling down
this twinding road,
Ya got to
"get down"
to carry your load

Because only then,
can you learn to win

~When the time is right~

There doesn't
seem much left,
be bereft,
here comes the night

As a deeper
blend of hues
imbues,

slowly, subtly
fading to black:
transforming images;
quite a sight!

Look quick,
over your back,
to, perchance,
catch a glimpse of:
the reaper

He appeared one day
(I was in bed),
and I suddenly
craved coffee,
but chose *tea* instead

Having read of
"Red",
and *his* famous
family recipe:
An orange spice
variety

His son, Red Junior,
then plunged the
bold blade
of his canary-yellow
Bouie knife
into the trunk
of a green, Grecian tree

As overhead flew
blue bird,
HIS son,
Red the third,
skipped
aqua coloured stones
on the silvery surface
of an indigo sea

The dapper, dappled waves
breaking,
and taking
the smooth stones in

Shades of violet
twilight
shone down where he wades
in the *thickness,*
with a *quickness*

The third stone skipped
seven times
landing deftly upon
metal tine
(~tink~)

What do you
(~think~)
Of azure, cobalt, and
baby too?

There are so many marvelous
shades of blue!

It is so special,
that it knows:
two slots in the
"Royal Rainbow"

With red, orange, yellow,
and a green too,
but for the next shade,
there are two:
indigo, and blue
finishing with violet, true

So, as these forces
you employ,
give thought for the 'morrow

For you can only experience joy:
to the depth which
you have felt sorrow

Never forget to
pay your dues
as you *live* out
this bizarre
blend of blues

Be not afraid,
to get your feet wet
as *you* slowly wade
into life's palette

In all that you do,
add color and flair
throw in a bold
dash of blue,
and you will be:
well balanced,
alive, and
aware!

"Take it, take another little piece of my heart now, baby!"
Joplin
"I'm the one that's got to die when it's time for me to die"
Hendrix
"People are strange, when you're a stranger" Morrison

"In order to play the *blues,* ya gotta *live the blues*"
Brother Badger

A Ping-Pong Sound

My 1st poem, written at the age of 8

Once I heard
A ping-pong-ping
I said to myself,
"What is that thing?"

I looked here,
And I looked there
'Till I practically
Looked everywhere!

Finally,
I looked around,
A little ping-pong
Ball I found

So, I played with it
All day long
Because I heard
A "ping-pong, ping pong"

What Am I?

High school lesson: poem from the viewpoint of an inanimate object

I am a vast storehouse
    of knowledge and fact.
But sometimes I contain
    only that:
which is thought of
    by the minds
of men.

    Look into me
that I might look out,
    and see the many expressions:
happiness and joy,
    sadness and fear;

but mostly awe, and understanding.
    For if it is to ME you look, you are looking in
a ______.

This was an assignment in creative writing in high school, written
2/12/84

Holidays Past

Holidays ~
Now they just
Come and go
Like
So many impatient people,

Trying to sell something
(Anything)

Mister Time, turn back
The hands, if you please . . .

Let me say the things
That I really meant

Let me give the freckled girl
Standing, waiting,
Something to smile about

And, if naught,
Let me at least
Be content with the thought
That children everywhere
Are enjoying so immensely
That there's some left over.

Not much,

But just enough for me to
Tuck away, so I can
Sniff it, once a year . . .

Written on 12/14/84 In a creative writing class

The Lamentations of a Little Lost Laddie

My Biography

Chapter I

The day I got lost walking home from kindergarten

I

I am soaring in ether. There are friendly "beings" all around me. I can hear them talking to each other, but I cannot speak. There is a bright, illuminating light shining all around us. They are talking about me, and there is a great expectation in the air; and a sense of urgency. I am suddenly moving at great speed toward a bright, blue sphere. Then I am floating in a languorous liquid darkness, infused with soft silky light. I hear noises, but I have very few conscious thoughts or understanding of these strange things. Then, in trauma, I enter the cold, noisy light.

II

I am so happy. Everyone around me is smiling and laughing, my mommy and daddy, and my two older brothers. I am ecstatic as I take my first steps; such a feeling of wonderful freedom! Very shortly after that, I am running, roaming, and reading.

I entered kindergarten in September of nineteen sixty-nine at Cambridge Elementary school, in Concord, California. I love school because our teacher reads stories to us, and makes the noises of the animals and characters that she reads about. She also plays the piano and we sing songs. I like the one about the kangaroo. I develop a love for the dulcet tones as they sound from the beautiful instrument; they seem to float in the air like sweet little birds.

My mommy takes me to school in our grey Volkswagen beetle. Sometimes I lay in the back on the grey, prickly carpet and look up at the clouds. They look like fluffy bunnies.

Then, after looking at some different houses, we moved to a house on Clayton Road. I liked the different houses that we looked at; one of my favorites was one that was right on the corner. It had a thick, green lawn, pretty yellow curtains tied up in the kitchen window, and a tree out front that looked like it had red curly crepe paper all over its trunk.

I switched to Ayers Elementary school; I was still in Kindergarten. Because we lived close to the school, on my third day there, my mommy walked to school to pick me up, and walked me home.

We talked about what I had done that day, and I told her that I was excited because tomorrow, I was going to make something called a plaster hand cast. She told me that I was her "little" man, and that I was old enough to start walking home all by myself. I was very excited about being so grown up, but I was also already a little apprehensive.

The next day, by the end of class, I was out front standing with my little hand on the red brick wall waiting for my mommy. When she did not show up, I started crying. A nice lady from the principal's office came out and asked me what was wrong. When I told her, she got my mommy on the phone. I talked to her, and she said,

"Darren, you are a big boy, and I want you to walk home just like we did yesterday. I thought that you understood that? I have cookies in the oven, and can't come to get you. So come right home, be careful, and you can have some cookies and milk while you tell me about your day. I love you"

So I handed back the phone on its green stretchy cord, and prepared to walk home. I was proud of the hand cast that I had made that day, and I made sure that it was safely packed in my bag with my books and papers. Before I did, I took it out and admired it one last time, placing my hand back into the cool, hard plaster.

I started home, but I was so distraught that I got lost. I was terrified! I saw some teenagers, and they were laughing. They asked me where I lived, and I tried to tell them, but they just walked away and left me all alone. I was miserable. I remember walking by a house that had a big hedge in front. I was looking at the bush when a big black dog suddenly jumped and started barking at me.

I dropped my hand cast and it broke! Then I really started bawling, walking blindly. Suddenly through my tears, I saw the green house with the yellow curtains and the tree out front with crepe paper on it. I sat down on the corner, a weary, lonesome lost laddie. Then I heard a familiar sound: the unmistakable rumble of a Volkswagen engine! I saw my mommy pull up, get out, and wrap me in her arms. She was crying too.

She took me home, wrapped me in a fluffy woolen blanket, and rocked me until I stopped crying, cooing how sorry she was in my ear. Then we had fresh, warm snicker-doodles and milk.

Darren and the Giant Locust

Chapter II

Born on April twentieth, nineteen sixty-three at Washoe Medical Center, in the biggest little city in the world, Reno, Nevada. I was the third boy born to my loving and attentive parents, entitling me to not only be "the baby", but to be spoiled not only by my mommy and daddy, but aunts, uncles, grandparents, etc.

I was born prematurely, as were my two older siblings. It seems that my mother had a hard time carrying to full term, and I know that I have a couple of other siblings that were born first that did not survive.

We moved shortly thereafter to Folsom, California, and these are some of my memories there, around the age of three to five. I was standing in a room right next to the sliding glass door to the patio, admiring my father's oak gun cabinet. It was a little over twice my height, and I could have stacked eight of me inside.

I was noticing the difference between the smooth glass of the sliding door to the patio, and the rippled look to the glass on the double locking doors of the rifle cabinet. As I looked at the contents behind the glass, the image that I perceived was slightly distorted, or rippled, kind of what it looks like when you put a stick in the water.

My daddy told me that his antique cabinet had come around Cape Horn, the tip of Chile, in South America. This was before the Panama Canal had been built. He explained that the panes were handmade, as opposed to the machine made glass that was on the patio doors. That accounted for the irregularity that I noticed.

He is a good mentor, always encouraging my curiosity by complimenting me not only on my ability to notice the difference, but also the awareness to ask why.

Standing with one hand on the smooth, cool wood, and the other clutching an Oscar Meyer hot dog. (I developed an early love of processed meats.)
As I stood there pondering the altered images of my dad's fascinating rifles, it occurred to me that my body was self-sustaining; I was becoming aware of the mechanism of my autonomous nervous system. I wondered how long I could stand there not consciously breathing before my body took over and induced an inhalation. The light headedness that I was experiencing seemed to accentuate the perturbation of the image.

We lived on Avon Way, and my uncle, aunt, and cousins lived right up the hill and around the corner. Respectively, Uncle Terry, Aunt Dee and her two children, Rodney and Theresa (Who we called "Cricket" at the time), and the one boy that they had together, my cousin Michael.

I was enjoying some salty sunflower seeds, emulating my dad: I would but a small hand full in my mouth, and crack them one at a time with my front teeth, spit the shell out, and eat the kernel.

Walking up the hill, humming, spitting, and chewing, I stepped up onto the covered front door step and rang the bell, excited at the prospect of playing with my kin. As my finger was pushing the button, my eyes wandered to the welcome mat.

There by the wall was a huge grasshopper, looking right back at me. I was fascinated by his eyes, which seemed to be surveying me benignly. All of the sudden he spooked and jumped what seemed to be fifty feet high! This was so unexpected that I panicked, dropped my cellophane package, and ran home crying!

That scene replayed in my dreams that night, but instead of being frightened- (my dad told me that I could control my dreams and do anything that I wanted), I hopped on the accommodating guy's back, and he took me to meet The King and Queen of the locusts. After that, I was no longer frightened, and whenever I saw another grasshopper, I greeted them in the name of The King and Queen, and told them that if they wanted to jump, they could do so and I would no longer be afraid.

Happy Hands

Isn't it clever?
Isn't it grand?
I've got a thumb and four fingers,
on each of my hands

When I play "cat's cradle",
they entertain with a string ~
(With these ten I can do,
just about anything)

When I play a game,
they might roll the dice-
and when I'm in the kitchen,
they might peel, flip, or slice!

When I'd like some music,
they can play my guitar ~
and when I go to the store
they can help drive my car!

When I comfort my friend,
they can pat on the shoulder.
And when the movie ends,
they are a tissue holder!

When I say goodbye,
They can get kind of wavy;
and when I'm fixing dinner,
they can help stir the gravy . . .

If your “one of the guys ”,
they stand like proud men-
(And they sure come in handy,
when counting to ten . . .)

But if you’re a gal,
they’re like ten pretty girls :
they dance and they sway,
they laugh and they twirl!

When I go outdoors,
they can put on my hat;
they can help walk the dog
or put out the cat

What they’ll do next,
only time will tell ~
but I think that we’ll always
get along just swell!

Mother's Way

(The Birds and the Bees)

'Tis grand to behold
a summer breeze,
hot soup when it's cold
a laugh, a sneeze

A blossoming tree
by dawn's early light,
the buzz of a bee
in purposeful flight

Some cool lemonade
in the afternoon;
the light which shines
from a full harvest moon

The languorous time
of evenings' rest;
a meaningful rhyme,
a hummingbird's nest

But when a child
enters this world,
tender and mild,
the future unfurled,

It's surely the best
occasion of all!
To look on his face,
cherubic and small

You'll suckle your son
held close to your breast,
it will give you great joy
to offer your best!

Instilling good traits
you'll teach with finesse,
and open the gates
which lead to success

Then tucking in bed
at the end of the day
"Good night, sleepy-head",
loving, in mother's way

Written for my niece, Lindsay, and her first born, Austin.

The Diamond

While drifting through a mysterious dream,
a pale sparkle caught my eye
and knowing that things were not as they seem,
it eluded me, much as I tried

Slowly revolving, I saw a reflection ~
a fey apparition sublime
and kneeling in reverent genuflection,
I felt strangely frozen in time

Arising, attempting in vain, to clear,
an obscuring cloud from my vision
Was the won'drous face so painfully near
reality, or merely illusion?

Feelings of apprehension and dread,
washed over me in a black wave
for a moment I feared I was dead,
as I saw myself in a shallow grave

I detected a rose scented perfume then,
a scent from someplace long ago
from a special place, I remembered not when -
it seemed vaguely familiar, though

At this point I heard a beckoning sound,
as sweet as a silver bell ~
it came from a distance, I found,
but through time or space, I could not tell

As I turned to the sound, I beheld a sight
that warmed my soul to the bone
it was your face I saw, and I thought that I might
like to somehow have you for my own

I desperately tried to give you a sign,
as things moved in painful slow - motion
numbness was seizing my mind
and I felt as if under the ocean

I saw your lips move, but I heard not a sound
I knew you were trying to reach me
there was symbolism all around,
I wondered what it was trying to teach me

I was abruptly transported to a distant land,
to a long-ago person I'd known
As that person looked down at his hand,
I saw that the hands were my own!

When I looked up, you were there on the shore
holding a mystical shell ~
You held it to my ear: I heard the oceans roar,
but, as I reached for your hand, you fell!

It seems you had enchanted me, lifetimes ago,
and our destinies entwined together
through successive lives we would learn and grow,
and grow wiser through storms that we weathered

And as each time that, by fate, our paths crossed,
and we pooled together our abilities -
- cleaving that which we gained, *leaving* that which we lost,
slowly weaving a complex tapestry

Once when I was a sailor, you made my rope,
our trades seemed to complement each other
then you provided me with much needed hope,
when, in one life, you were my *Mother*

When I was a merchant, you were a buyer
and when I raised horses, you rode well -
when I wrote music, you sang in a choir,
when I *raced horses* , you rang the bell!

Once you were drowning, and I saved your life
and as I pulled you out of the water
I knew that one day, you would be my wife,
and that we would raise a son and a daughter

As each successive scene was revealed,
mysterious truths were uncovered:
facts came to light which had once been concealed,
as the purpose for life I discovered

I found myself working in an African mine
at gems I attempted to quarry
I had found one that appeared to be one of a kind,
but this was just the *start* to this part of the story

In my *next life* I encountered that very same rock,
and cut it into a faceted treasure
I stored it carefully away in a *strong box*,
knowing it would one day give great pleasure!

After that I wore a jeweler's shoes,
large profits attempting to lure -
and at one point I made a *magnificent* ring,
from a gem I'd felt compelled to procure

~II~

At this point in time, from my dream I awoke,
and marveled at the people I'd been
But the memories slowly dissipated like smoke,
as I tried in vain to recall all that I'd seen

I went out to a party that night,
and by chance, met a *beautiful* girl
her olive eyes had an enchanting light,
that hypnotized me with each two-step and whirl

As we got better acquainted, I could not shake the feeling,
that I'd somehow known her before -
and my future with her, she was surely sealing,
with the rose scented perfume she wore

So one night while deserting on peaches and cream,
I planned what our future should bring -
so I went to a place that I'd seen in a dream,
and bought a *magnificent* ring

Then on a bright July day we were married,
as it was with *you* that I desired to linger -
and I thought to myself, "Too long we had tarried",
as I placed that ring on your finger . . .

Then as from that gem, sunlight reflected,
an ancient *pact* between us passed -
I knew that my once scattered thoughts had collected,
and that I'd found my *soul-mate* at last

You see life, like that ring, has no end or beginning,
as these lives connect one to another
and as the wheel of life is inexorably turning,
it's our *duty* to *look out* for *each other*

There is a perfect spark in our soul, directly from God
and since energy is neither
destroyed nor *created*;
we've always been here in one form or *another*,
and to improve and evolve we are fated

So remember, as the wheel of life revolves,
it can only help your soul to be kind -
nice folk who follow this law will evolve,
but mean folk that don't will be *left behind*

Destiny's Dance

"Every man gotta right to choose his own destiny" Bob Marley

Rhyming with reason,
shifting dunes of time
A purposeful season,
with fullness, sublime

To burn, perchance,
this poignant fire;
we partake of
"The Dance",
with deep, dark desire

Wherefore is the truth
of *life*, *liberty*, and *pursuit*
abundant in youth,
resoundingly mute

Driven with force,
cunning and haste,
the chariot and horse,
prepare for the race

Embracing the law,
conforming and sure
and arising, I saw
the *chosen*, the pure~

Will *time* now mend,
the flaw that is me?
And will the bird send,
over tempestuous seas-

A message clear,
that we understand?
To our hearts, hold dear,
As we claim this land

These spirits knew,
that which was *known*
The Chosen, the few -
their seed we have sewn

And some of the souls
intent on free reign,
were reincarnate, and then
in strength did remain

Trapped inside
these earthen vessels,
in search of pride,
with mortality, wrestled

The phantoms are *restless*
as they fly in the night;
soaring in reckless,
abandoned delight

(~wherever they linger,
an eerie blue light~)

Arose up in numbers,
with unmistakable power
now pausing,
each member,
did wait for the hour

With keen intent
and inevitable will,
they will invent,
enact, and fulfill

~Destiny's Dance~

Listen! Look! Learn!
Free will, love, and purpose,
are treasures to earn

For the fire consumes that
which is forgotten, yet left
burned into the hearts
of the lost and bereft

For in the physical act,
we will discover
the ***mysterious pact,***
that ~~DEATH~~ was our lover . . .

A piece that I wrote quickly in 1998, then edited in 2017

Another Year

A Birthday poem for my dad. June 6th, 2009

Another year has passed you by,

Don't cry, don’t cry,

Now it's time to raise your staff;

Let’s laugh, let’s laugh!

It's time to realize the wonder:

Let’s ponder, let’s ponder . . .

Now it’s time to give,

Let’s Live, let’s live

Look up into the air:

Let’s prepare, let’s prepare

Things are not as they seem;

Let’s dream, let's dream~

Put an end to all the strife,

Let’s enjoy life!

Mr. Darren and Recovery

Chapter III

I Live at North Side Recovery, in Del Paso Heights, a suburb of Sacramento, California. From 2012 to September of 2016, I lived by the Feather River in Marysville, CA, which is about an hour N of here. I moved here to Sacramento for a number of reasons: I like it here, there are great resources, and I needed to get away from the drug scene, from which I had been suffering as an intra-venous methamphetamine user for twenty-four years.

I started by checking myself into Sierra Vista Mental Hospital. I had been there before, and I knew that they would take good care of me. Since I had just had a hernia surgery, they sent me from there to Mercy General Hospital, where I received the most gentle and loving care. I mostly slept and healed.

My next stop was for two months at Heritage Oaks Mental Hospital. There I got the tools that I needed to enjoy recovery, and I knew that they would not release me until I had a stable place to live. I met some very interesting people there, and I got the opportunity to share my love of life, my poetry, and my music, as I had my guitar, and performed.

I got out in December 2015, and moved into Midtown Independent Living. Because I had literally lost everything (but my guitar) to my addiction, I had no identification. So, I had to go back to Marysville to my bank to get rent money. I was firm in my resolve to quit using, but meth is such a crafty and cunning enemy that I suffered a relapse.

I told myself, "You are doing so well, a couple of hits is not going to hurt you". Three days of hell later, I found that NOT to be the case.

I went from there to a house on Thomas Street, in North Highlands, with what I thought was a stronger resolve. Heritage Oaks Hospital had set me up with this living condition also. It was a beautiful, large house in North Highlands, Sacramento (a suburb of Sacramento) with a nice green lawn and fragrant Jonquils blooming out front. When I arrived at around 9:00 PM, I was met by a friend that I had met at Heritage Oaks, Daniel. He was also on SSI, and he got money on his card every Wednesday.

He was my room-mate, and when he got his money, the first thing that he did was buy an eight-ball. This is slang for 1/8th of an ounce, or three point five grams. Well, there went all my resolve again. I just could not get away from it, and it was driving me crazier! So, disgusted, weary, and even more strung out, I sought solace at L to L sober living, near Auburn and Watt Avenue.

I stayed there, and it was a much more stable environment. I was required to attend three NA meetings a week. It was a beautiful house in the suburbs, and I really started enjoying sobriety. I was surrounded by recovering addicts, and we all worked together to stay clean one day at a time.

My next stop was the best, Northside Recovery. Now, don't get me wrong, I would very much like to have a place of my own, and enjoy those comforts, but this is where God has me, and I embrace that. He told me that I was to prosper in that which He would have me to do, and to share the blessings that I have and the talents that I have been blessed with.

I am so very thankful, I was raised with old school values: honor, integrity, courtesy, honesty, pride in your family name, and hard work. Having this thankful attitude, just when I think that things have leveled out into a comfortable plateau, He takes me even higher!

Now I have a great job conducting surveys for an independent polling firm, and with the resources that I have available, I am able to enrich and bless not only my life, but the lives of all those around me. I love to cook, and there is a gas oven and stove at the house.

My first payday, I bought a prime rib, and cooked it with all the trimmings, green beans with bacon, onion, and tomatoes, my special smashed garlic potatoes with cream cheese and sour cream with a parmesan crust, and berry pie with fresh whipped cream for dessert. Everyone there loves and looks up to me, especially my roommate, Curtis. He is very special to me, and God put me here to help take care of him. He also is a recovering addict, who lost one eye to a bullet wound. His addiction took him far away, and he no longer even knows how to contact any of his family members.

Another thing that has greatly helped me in my recovery is, since the person who conducted the Wed. night NA meetings left, I filled in and took over. After a lot of upheaval and changes at the house, all of the meetings were stopped. Tomorrow night, I will be starting the NA meeting up again, but now it is voluntary, not mandatory.

To show my appreciation for how well the guys are doing, I made French dip sandwiches and my special smashed potatoes with plenty of Au jus and rich brown gravy, and told them this is the type of gourmet cooking that you will enjoy WHEN you decide to attend my meetings. Honey attracts more bees than vinegar! I am happy, blessed, and fulfilled. I have let go and let God, and He is taking me on a wild ride that is honestly enjoyable, not fake and short lived, like the drugs.

I know that addiction is a progressive disease, because it just got worse and more miserable. Now thing are improving exponentially. I have a future, which is bright and fulfilling.

Jeremiah 29:11 states,
"For I know the thoughts that I think toward you, saith the LORD, thoughts of peace, and not of evil, to give you an expected end."

I am living proof, and February 4th, 2017 will be my one year birthday.

Autumn's Gold

Autumn leaves are drifting down,
like snowflakes soon to come
Bright mosaics on the ground,
bare branches where they're from.

Richly coloured hues of gold
come dancing to the earth;
fiery flames that lick the cold-
of mother nature's hearth

Singing sadly one last time
the Robin, breast of red,
spreads her wings for warmer clime
(The ground is cold and dead)

As the wheel of life revolves
and seasons run their course,
the saga quickens, turns: evolves
an ever changing force

Weary cold and blue, I cry
away the robin flies
Summer shrugs and bids good-bye,
as all that lives must die

Barren cold and bleak, the land,
still holds the promise of -
blossoms sweet and living grand,
and blessings from above!

Silently I watch the scene
from in my quiet room.
Feeling small, my thoughts serene,
I'm safe within my womb

As I close my eyes I pray:
to dream of summer clouds;
and then upon a fragrant day,
escape from winter's shroud!

I wrote this in 2000, and looking back, I can see that it is a metaphor for my addiction. I am currently living the last stanza.

This is the first poem that I wrote in this stage of my life at the age of thirty-seven, and set the stage for all of the writing that follows . . .

Bedbugs and Character Flaws

Chapter IV

How Mr. Darren learned to control his anger

Dedicated to all in recovery. Keep up the good work! If you are like me in this way, then you know that some things can only be accomplished the hard way!

When you enter the world of recovery, you are faced with a new lease on life; you get to "re-invent" yourself, shedding the bad habits and slowly, painfully, replacing them with new, constructive and life skill building ones. In this process, one must learn about one's "character" flaws, those evil skeletons hiding in our closets that have manipulated and controlled our negative behaviors for so long. The reason that they are so hard to identify and change is because they are so firmly engrained in our personality, like years of crusty barnacles and grime cemented to the underside of a seagoing vessel.

Mr. Darren found out quickly that one of his main flaws was, (is, still working on it!), ANGER. Styx put it very succinctly in a song off the 1977 album, "Grand Illusion" called "Fooling Yourself (Angry Young Man)", "Why must you be such an angry young man, when your future looks quite bright to me?" I found that the one that I am angriest at is me!

This is the letter that I wrote:

To Whom It may Concern:
This is the story of bedbugs (and other) problems that I have experienced at North Side Recovery. The problem started in June of 2016. The bugs were a problem and it was all that Bill G., the day manager, could do to keep up with the constant complaints. He was treating the mattresses with powder. I kept having problems, and on the evening of May 31st, it came to a head!

I came back after the first meeting that I had missed since my residency (there are three mandatory meetings, T, W, and Thursday, and I had been so tired from lack of sleep that I fell asleep on the bike trail and inadvertently missed the meeting)

When I complained that the bugs had been biting me, the day manager, Doc, said that it was all in my head! At that point I attempted to contact Bill G, but he was not available, so I called the owner, Bill B. He got angry with me, so I told him that I needed to see him in person, and hung up on him. He came in very angrily and ordered me in to the office. He then proceeded to state that they had checked for bugs in my area, and found none. When I told him that I had killed one, and had been repeatedly bitten, he said, "Show me the bug! Show me the bites!" I was livid by now, and I lost my temper and said something very rude!

Well, I was then, not so cordially, invited to grab what I needed immediately, and leave the premises and come back for the rest of my stuff the next day. I apologized vehemently and asked if he would reconsider, to no avail.

I found another clean and sober living place right away, but to my horror, found that this place too was infested with the little vampires. What to do?! So, I put my belongings in storage, and went back to live at an area by the river that I was familiar with, close to CSUS. I am very proud of myself, because I had enough sobriety under my belt, I was exposed to meth more than once during my stay at the river, but I never gave in, remembering how horrible my other two relapses had been. I was just thoroughly enjoying a clear state of mind for the first time in many years!

On the afternoon of June 31st, Bill G texted me and told me that he had a bed open, and that I could return to North Side. I immediately accepted the offer, and moved back in, much to the pleasure of all there, especially my good friend and roommate Curt. When I asked Bill how it was that I was invited back, he said, "I told Bill that I was inviting you back, and he grumbled, but agreed that I know what is best"

Another factor that I believed helped was my improved professional attitude. Because a storage payment had been stolen out of the mail box, I was short on rent, and owed about $225.00. Now, I could have said screw them, but I did not, and after I was kicked out, I returned to make a payment of one third the amount of the balance. After I returned, I was told to forget about the remaining balance. Hallelujah!

On Thursday, July 14th the whole house was treated for pests. When I returned that evening, I found three live bedbugs on and around my mattress. I placed them in a zip-lock bag, and reported the incident to Doc. On Friday the 15th in the evening, I received eight bites altogether, and by now I was very wary, and had the sense to document them with date stamped pictures from my phone. Not wanting to be bitten any more, I slept on the couch for the rest of the evening. (Which is against the rules!)

The next day Bill G was off, so Bill B came in at 6:00 AM and demanded to know what I was doing sleeping on the couch. When I told him that I was still getting bitten, he exploded and said that he had just spent a large amount of money getting rid of the pests, and that it was probably me that was bringing in the little blood suckers. Now, the old me would have reacted with anger, BUT the new me said, politely, "Yes sir, not a problem, sir, it won't happen again sir"

Fortunately Bill G showed up shortly thereafter and informed Bill B that it was not my fault, that there was in fact still a bug infestation. He told me that Bill B was not angry at me, he was angry at the whole situation, and for having paid for a service that was not completely rendered. I have been bitten now, humiliated, disrespected, and traumatized. I have sincerely apologized for my behavior, but had not gotten any back.

Then, a couple of days later, Bill B came up to ME and apologized! I found this to be a suitable reward and outcome for the pain and patience which I had invested, and it turned out to be a humbling experience for us both. Hallelujah!

I find it ironic that two of the traditions of Alcoholics Anonymous are to be capable of rigorous honesty, and when we were wrong, we promptly admitted it. Maybe Bill B's admittance was not so prompt, but in the grand scheme of things, it was a miraculous "gift" that I will remember and cherish for the rest of my life.

I really like it here at North Side Recovery, and truly believe and show through my actions, hard work, and genuine compassion that I am an asset to the environment. I would like to continue to live and participate in the program. I am writing this letter in hopes of a peaceful resolution. I just want to exist in a bug free environment, and get along with everybody.

I am sorry for losing my temper, and will do my best to work on that so that it does not happen again. I do not think that these are unreasonable requests. Thank-you so much for your help and continued support. Respectfully, Mr. Darren

And this is how Mr. Darren learned not only how to control his anger, but I have also done a lot of research on how to control bugs. Hallelujah!

Not Wild Jokerz

Take a toke
It's not a joke
that when you
choose to smoke

That you will find
that your mind
will *never be the same*

Step on a crack,
break your mother's back
but if you *smoke crack,*
you'll break your
mother's heart!

Don't you realize
that The Lord's eyes
are everywhere?

Listen to your inner voice:
it's wise, you *do* have a choice.

You are only dealt one hand in life,
don't fill it with drugged jokerz!
They're a little too wild,
(They're really *not* mild)

When you call on them,
they have already made
many decisions for you
have given them control

Don't choose to go into a hole
that you can
NEVER
GET
OUT OF!!!

And please beware
of the jokerz friends-
for although they
may appear
to mean well,
they are in that hole,

and would like very much for you
to join them there
but they are
LOST,
BLIND,
and CONFUSED

And have no right
corrupting a
fine and unpolluted
child of God
like yourself.

That wise and comforting
little voice
is always there.
Won't you please
lend it your ear?

Ourobouros ~ Fact or Fiction?

"Deep, unspeakable suffering may well be called a baptism, a regeneration, the initiation into a new state" Ira Gershwin

Is it reality,
or merely fiction?
Peer in the mirror,
and you will see:
the many faces
of your addiction

Strung along
in its saddest song
prepare to be
tempted and tossed

A blue note *plays*;
time signature *delays*,
you suddenly notice you're lost!

In a deep, dark trance
that fluctuates wildly.
"It's just my circumstance",
you think, mildly

As you blindly grasp for
the next "head change",
a quick fix-mix

The landscape *changes,*
cell structure rearranges,
a slow, sickening remix

You find yourself *dreaming,*
day, and night;
all of them seeming
to change from "fun" to "fright",
to outright not turn out right.

But you put on a brave face,
and face that reflection;
it sneers and snarls
in dereliction

You shone in your youth,
but now deny truth
as you row
in the wrong direction

Long ago, when you
first tested the *waters,*
starting with the toes;
then you dove in like an otter!

You frolicked and played,
then swept away
in the *current;*
It felt good that day,
but IS a
current deterrent

Slipping deeper into
the *murky quagmire*,
trying to just stay afloat
getting exponentially tired,
trapped in a
discordant moat

It appears that some
seem not to mind,
muddling up their mind;
while "these others"
like it clearheaded

Lend me your ear
fend off your fear,
and LOOK at
where you are headed!

Do like "these"
and not like "those";
stop consuming yourself
like
Ourobouros!

Wanting desperately
to get *wired*
while all the while
you *admire*
your lovely, fatal *fire*
and the flames are
licking *higher*

You're starting to *perspire*
they are calling you a *liar,*
gleefully leaping
through your *pyre*,
that could be funereal.

Is that your
true desire?

Ouroboros (disambiguation).

The Ourobouros is an ancient symbol depicting a serpent or dragon eating its own tail. Originating in Ancient Egyptian iconography, the Ourobouros entered western tradition via Greek magical tradition and was adopted as a symbol in Gnosticism and Hermeticism, and most notably in alchemy. Via medieval alchemical tradition, the symbol entered Renaissance magic and modern symbolism, often taken to symbolize introspection, the eternal return or cyclicality, especially in the sense of something constantly re-creating itself. It also represents the infinite cycle of nature's endless creation and destruction, life and death.

~~~~~~

Addiction is a serious disease that "strings you along", thinking that you can function. At first, it seems possible, but for 99.9% it IS a progressive condition that worsens continually. With this excerpt,

In a deep, dark trance
that fluctuates wildly.
"It's just my circumstance",
you think, mildly

I am illustrating that one of the worst symptoms of this illness is that it eventually causes an "apathy", to where you no longer care what it is doing to you, and everything that you come into contact with.

June 7, 2017 Brother Badger
~~~~~~

Infinite Love

He loves us so much,

that He gave His only Son

so that we *might* live

He's got the whole world

planet earth is round

and this is what I have found:

that His love surrounds

Peace on Earth

if I was a bird

I would be a snow white dove

representing peace

The Gift of Forever

A Secret Christmas message

Can you feel the love,

He sends from above?

Realize the wonder

Is it growing stronger?

Seeing our cost

There on the cross

May we not sever

A gift of forever

Sent on the wings

of a Dove

Good Tidings

A message of hope and cheer,
during this festive time
For 'tis the time of the year
to share a Yuletide rhyme

After all the shopping is done,
the wrapping and the cards;
all the calls to everyone,
wishing warm regards!

Now all is ready to go,
and it's time to rest-
Time to change to SLOW,
and in *slumber* invest

And as we close our eyes
we pray for safe repose
His help to be *wise,*
and in His Spirit, grow

The fragrant trce, so tall
glimmering in the light
Merry Christmas to all,
and to all a good night!

A New Star

The holy time that is right now,
and every Christmas past-
a festive, warm, and timely show
that always goes too fast!

Trifles, treats, and treasures
all around the tree,
displayed in generous measures,
a pretty sight to see

Angelic voices, caroling
songs written for the day
Soft snow falling, heralding
the Boy birthed in the hay

The cattle softly lowing
a New Star shining bright-
its heavenly light showing:
mankind's new found delight!

The vibrant vision, laid before
those present at the stable;
a gift that's free, for rich and poor
for all those who are able:

to accept the best reward
that was never earned-
offered from our faithful Lord,
a lesson to be learned

To be called are many,
but chosen are a few;
so always offer plenty
in everything you do!

Perhaps some may feel differently,
but they appear not wise;
for it seems they do not see
that His love IS the prize

I know He wants to cherish
all who find His grace;
that none should die and perish
when we leave this earthly place

So, if you are reading,
preparing for your rest;
know that we're all needing
to be truly blessed!

Treat others as you would yourself
and try not to grumble-
for whosoever exalts himself,
shall in the end be humbled

Put your worries on a shelf,
your neighbor shan't be faulted;
for he that humbleth himself
shall surely be exalted!

A Christmas Paradox

As I lay in bed thinking about the coming holidays, I was filled with both a sense of joy and wonder, and of gloom and dread. Joy because I am a holiday type of guy, and dread because I was very poor, and was acutely worried that, by not living up to my full potential that Santa was going to leave me a stocking full of coal! (Which would not be all bad, at least I could heat my meager bungalow for a few days) And besides, to be quite honest I was more likely to be on his "naughty" list, as opposed to nice. ~ : - (

Since people say that I am as mad as a hatter, (THE mad hatter? Why should it matter?) , my head always churns with percolating thoughts of whimsy and fantasy when I lay down to rest (Purple mushrooms, green clovers), Str-e-t-ch, yawn, scratch, (cats, mice, tropical toucans), eyes getting heavy, no use fighting it, (aborigine pygmies, giant rainbow kaleidoscope snowflakes, vast green pristine lawns covered with sparkling dew-drops of sunlight) . . . (snore. . .) . . . Unkkkkkkkk, whoooooooo, Unkkkkkkkk, whooooo, Unnkkkkkkkkkkk, whoooooooooooo

I am floating, serene. My eyes are closed. I detect no stimulus along my optic nerve, but somehow I know that I am drifting languorously over a pristine green English lawn . . . Suddenly I am sucked into a rabbit hole; much as a radiant, stray particle of light is plucked from space into a black hole . . . I hear a bizarre mixed up medley of Jerry Garcia, Johnny cash, and Engelbert Humperdink music . . .With a crisp, crackly crunching noise, I suddenly landed with my eyes wide open on a vast, barren, and precipitous plain.

As I squinted my eyes into the harsh rays of the rising sun, I felt that I was being watched by a dark mysterious stranger in a pea green trench coat. But when I turned around, there was nobody there. I must distract myself (a useful behavior that I pride myself on), so I turn back around.

In front of me are two large canvas tents that are a disconcertingly paranoid shade of rust. There is something metallic looking nestled betwixt them, but it is hard to see, as my eyes are still watering from the cruel sunlight.

I walk slowly to the tent on the left, much as a humble supplicant would approach a malevolent magistrates gaveling, and slowly lift the dry wind-blown flap. Inside, I smell an unpleasant pungent iron odor, but am relieved to be out of the wind and sun. There is music playing from an ancient wind-up phonograph, and the grating, tinny sound reminds my ears of what the sunlight was like to my eyes. It is some bizarre Indian or Hindu music that I do not recognize, and I find myself wondering at its origin. (Past life? Bohemian coffee shop? Delusion?)

There is a dark polished mahogany bar, and for a moment I almost get lost in the wholesomely welcoming whirls of wood. As I walk up to the bar and put my weathered boot onto the worn brass foot rail, I am suddenly filled with terror, as I am a grievous alcoholic. I experienced the anxiety that one has when one has conquered a severe problem, and then finds themselves suddenly confronted with that very problem, and it seems like they are going to succumb.

To my calming relaxation, however, the pudgy balding barkeep set not a cocktail in front of me, but rather a pewter mug of warm milk. I do not want to risk eye contact, but it seems there is a dark stranger watching me from the other corner of the room. So, I acted like I was tying my (boot lace?!), and stole a quick glance in that direction on my way back up. He suddenly acted like he was going to nonchalantly take a drink from his mug, but it was an obvious deception, as his mug was full of iron-red dirt.

Suddenly, the music changed to a slow and wheedling version of "*Pop*! *Goes The Weasel*". I hear cat noises (Of which there really are many, if you stop to think about it), and face a split decision: I am quite fond of cats, but my other personality is terrified of them. So, I (I?) decide to take control of the situation by threatening my other self to chill, or it will be another stint in the subconscious dungeon.

So, as I turn around, I see sleek silver cats crawling out of a teapot. As they stretch and preen and peer at me the way cats will, their attention is abruptly diverted by mice, which are scurrying out through mouse-holes which are located in the floor-boards. The mice are strangely dull in coloration, almost as if they are, tarnished? And the strangest little goats (?) are coming out now too, at a ratio of 4: 1 (mice: goats)

Not being able to assimilate the absurdity if this irregular scene, I decide to turn back around and drink some of my milk. As I raise the tarnished pewter mug to my lips, I find that the milk tastes . . . different, maybe slightly sweet (?), so I put it down and head for the parched flap.

As I am reaching the crux of my departure, I notice an antique oval mirror on the far wall. It is about 10 feet high by 3 feet wide, and is framed by an intricately crafted ornamental oriental brass frame. I am tempted to check my hair and try and catch a secret glimpse of the dark stranger, but decide that that would probably be blowing it. (Do you ever find yourself wondering if you are blowing it? Yeah, me too)

So, I lifted the weathered flap and walked out into pale, frosty moonlight. (Some kind of time-warped fun-house. . . *(*Why, are *you* having fun?*)*) I felt that I needed to see what was in the other tent, hoping that it would hopefully have some semblance of normalcy to soothe my disturbed psyche. I walked over and was relieved to see that, although the canvas was also dry and weather-worn, it had apparently been treated with Thompson's water sealer, so it was in serviceable shape. I lifted the flap, much the way an expectant groom would lift the tender lace of his new brides veil, (why, you *are* having fun!), and entered. I had not prepared myself for the wondrous sight which I beheld: It was an authentic genuine Orchestral Polyphonic Strato-Various Tympanic Tickler guitar, complete with polished ebony body, reinforced rosewood neck, mother of pearl inlay, and gold-plated tuning pegs!

I knew everything there was to know about the Polyphonic Strato-Various, as there were detailed centerfold pinups of it on my wall, Limited Edition, only 300 of them lovingly made, and ultimately unattainable for a pauper such as myself. But, this was a dream, so I could do and have whatever I liked. I gently picked it up off its stand, and the ebony was so wonderfully polished that I could see the cast-iron frying pan full of fried potatoes that I was going to have for breakfast tomorrow, complete with parsley.

The Strato-Various is a model which was invented by the American musician / inventor Darren Gandy in the 21st century. Along with a classic electric guitar design, the sound is richly bolstered by *twelve* strategically placed pickups to provide the poly (many) phonic (sounding) acoustics. In addition, the bottom edge is pronounced to house a two-oscillator polyphonic synthesizer keyboard, complete with a wide range of effects which can be used and / or blended with the guitar to create a rich and complex combination of sounds.

I found that somehow I suddenly knew an interesting and complex Beethoven piece, and I played it with relish. Then I tried it with mustard, but somehow it just wasn't the same, so I put it down.

As I turned, I noticed an enticing circular red velvet curtain in the corner, much like the one that the Wizard of Oz hid behind to perform his many miraculous manifestations. I walked over and parted the curtain, and beheld a mirror *exactly like the one I had seen in the other tent.* Being a dirty white boy, I like to wash my face and keep my complexion clear. I am concerned about my reflection and my complex-ion, so I decided to check myself As I looked into the mirror, I saw myself looking back, *but I was black!!!*

It was me, but it wasn't me, because there seemed to be a delay before my reflection would do what I had done, and I had the eerie feeling that I was not looking at my reflection, but rather that my *reflection was looking at me* . . .How thoroughly flummoxed I felt! So, I tried a shy smile, and my reflection, after a moment of deliberation, gave the same expression, so I decided that it was most likely a further manifestation of my schizoid ideations, so I carefully turned away, lest I lose some of the 33 1/3 marbles that I have left. (I think I started with a boy-scouts full ration which is, what, 50? (I don't know, *you* tell me. . . (Just distract yourself-that's it, don't pay any attention to the man behind the curtain . . .AHHHHHHHHHHHhhhhhh!!*)*)

TURN AROUND AND WALK OUT SLOWLY. KEEP YOUR EXTREMITIES IN THEIR FULLY UPRIGHT POSITION, AND *JUST WALK AWAY. . .*

As I ran screaming for the water resistant tent flap, I felt certain that I had in fact lost two or three, I think. Anyway I play a little game with myself when confronted with such overwhelmingly horrifying simulations. I pretend that I am seated at the mad-hatter's tea party, and that I am busy moving down for another half of cup. (He never used to ask for *just* a half a cup . . .)

So, by the time that I reached the water-sealed flap, I had (I *am* getting rather good at this!) distracted myself sufficiently to move *away from the tent.* I got outside, and the moon had gone behind a cloud, much as it would on Halloween night in 1968 in a Detroit slum.

I felt weary and worn, and I wanted to find my way back to the warm, comforting safety of my cozy bed, lest I lose yet another valuable marble. I approached the edge of the precipice and stretched out my hands unto the frozen white wasteland, and took flight.

Somehow I navigated my way back to the opening to the (black?) rabbit hole, and was *extruded* through to the *other* side.

Once through, I heard The "Doors" playing: "*You know the day destroys the night, night divides the day, try to run, try to hide, Break on through to the Other Side! Break on through to the Other Side! Break on through to the Other Side, yeah . . ."* It was comforting to hear, much the way that a kindergarten-age child is comforted by his mother in a rocking chair after getting lost walking home from school, and barked at by a vicious dog, causing him to drop his little plaster hand cast and break it.

As I broke through the barrier between those two realities, and was emerging over the sparkling dew drops, I saw two chubby figures dressed like little children, complete with twirly propeller hats, standing back to back on the individual pristine grass blades. The one was facing me, and I had the uncomfortable feeling that as I passed, that he would make eye contact, thereby forcing a social interaction (much the way that a Catholic priest would pass a Baptist priest in front of a store which sells merchandise of questionable scruples), but he was in fact busy with a yo-yo. I noticed that the yo-yo had a yin-yang symbol on it. He wasn't necessarily paying close attention to the yo-yo, but nor was he really paying attention to anything, thus sparing me the uncomfortable interaction that I had wasted *way too much* energy worrying about. (Do you find yourself doing that? Yeah, me too) As I flew over, I saw that the other figure had a yo-yo, which he was also yo-yoing. But, I saw that instead of yo-yoing down, it was yo-yoing *up*. I admired his dexterity, as this is something that I had aspired to accomplish at one time in my youth.

It did not seem to be difficult at all to do, and as he performed the feat very deftly, I noticed two things: 1) His hands were *backwards*, that is to say, with the thumbs on the *inside* as his palms were face up (so that's the trick!), and, 2) That the yo-yo had the *opposite* design of his brother's. (A *yang-yin* symbol, guess.....?)

Finally I came to what looked like my neighborhood, but I wanted to stop by the mall and get a Josta Cola on the way home. When I walked into the mall, for some reason there were no stores, only a North Pole scene where some elves were busily milling about. I walked up, and Santa beckoned me to come forward. He looked very genuine, unlike a K-

Mart Santa. So, I approached him, with some trepidation, as you can imagine, (*naughty*, *naughty, naughty . . .),* and looked into his wise and ancient eyes.

"I know what you have been up to", he said benignly, "But you needn't worry, as you are an angel walking on earth. Sure, you may have made some mistakes, and do not feel like you are living up to your full potential, but you *do* have a very important and integral mission for your life, as we all do, and if you respect my counsel, advice, and instruction, you will successfully achieve a major breakthrough. Be of good cheer, as this will occur whether you cause it or not. But if you are able to approach the cusp with the proper attitude and desire to better yourself, you will truly break on through to the other side, and it be a glorious revelation. Now remember, in order to achieve this glorious goal, you will have to make some supreme sacrifices.

You will have to let go of something that is very valuable to you, and you will have to struggle very hard. It will be an excruciatingly painful process, but you have reached a point in your life where there is no turning-back. If you do not embrace and fulfill this change now, the place which you will find yourself in when you break-through will not be nearly as pleasant or as easy as the places which you *could* break through to. Sure, you will still have a purpose and will still be gifted and creative, but it will not be the same.

You see, we are inevitably the masters of our own destinies, and in that manner, we are endowed with the freedom to choose our own path. There are infinite paths to follow, and subsequently, infinite qualities of life.

There are *always* ways in which we can improve, and at some rare and major cusps in your life, a portal will open which will enable you to improve and expand in a *quantum leap*. For example, do you remember when you were learning to play the guitar? You worked diligently and hard, but were easily discouraged, and felt that you were not practicing or performing to your potential. Then one day, most naturally and unexpectedly, you were playing many, much more complex pieces, and, through hard work and a proper attitude, gained in a short time *ten times* more ability than you were previously capable of.

Or, when you took your first interest in drawing: you liked to draw, but your drawings were crude and, again, not to your liking / potential. Then one day, after working hard and approaching the cusp with the proper attitude, you set to work and produced a complex and intricate masterpiece. Actually, you do not know this, but your work was perceived in an alternate dimension, and a copy of that *very* picture hangs in "The Institute For Mental Healing", on a planet called Zarius Three, near a star known as Betelgeuse.

When it was first placed there, it performed a wondrous healing: during the second year of the Kunian Uprising, some rebels had stormed Great King Gwendaleir's fortress, and kidnapped his 10 year old daughter. She was subjected to grievous abuse and torture. Five years later, the King's armies finally defeated the rebels, and restored order to the war ravaged people, and the Princess was rescued and returned to the castle, much the way that a rare jewel is stolen and then returned to its velvet bed in its ornamental oriental antique display case. The princess, whose name was Lindra, was psychotic, and her personality was fragmented. The Doctors worked with her, and made some progress, but she was still very troubled, and could never be left alone. She pulled her hair out, and cried and moaned all day long.

The quantum leap came while being led by the hand from a therapy session by her nurse. She stopped and gazed at the picture, and her face transformed from a tortured grimace to a shy smile, and she shed her psychedelic psychosis.

The king was overjoyed, and declared a national holiday. (Which, incidentally, coincides with our Easter holiday)

You are at a point where you must use whatever means that you deem appropriate to learn more about the purpose for

your, and ultimately, all of our existences as we slowly perform this cosmic dance.
Remember these important concepts:
Attitude ~
Goals
Responsibility ~
Proper Perspective ~
Loss ~
Gain ~
Transformation ~
Reward ~ . . . ."

And as I heard his words fading into the recesses and compartments of my mind, I awoke.

II

I marveled at the intense visions which I had dreamt, but even as I scrambled to find a paper and pencil to jot some of it down, the memories dissipated like smoke. Oh well, I did wake feeling strangely more relaxed, refreshed, and invigorated than I had in a long time.

I got up, made my bed, and proceeded with my morning routine of getting cleaned up, eating, and reading the paper. As I was munching on my fried parsley potatoes, an interesting article caught my eye: it seemed that there was to be a musical contest at a local coffee shop. Grand prize was a weekend vacation to anywhere in the (non-communist) world!

So I grabbed my acoustic guitar, and headed over to "*Le Frond*"-a little Bohemian coffee shop that is in my neighborhood.

I played well, but was beaten by a beautiful woman that played a Celtic song so mournfully and beautifully that, by the time she had finished, there was nary a dry eye in the room.

So, I took my espresso outside, and sat down to play a piece.

As I was playing, the woman came out with her beverage, and asked if she could sit down.

I stood up and said,

"You are certainly welcome to join me. My name is Darren, and I must say that the piece that you played evoked images from my past lives. Congratulations on your victory, you were certainly the best musician"

"Thank you very much", she replied grasping my hand warmly.

"My name is Clara, and I must say that in all modesty, I thought that *you* deserved to win. Your playing has a healing quality which really helped me."

"Thank-You", I said, blushing.

We sipped our beverages companionably, and she asked me to play another song. I played a song I had written called, "The Distant Shore", and she quickly picked up the chorus and sang it with me in clear, sweet harmony:

> "*As together we rowed, and sang songs of truth*
> *We knew that the future would hold so much more*
> *Basking in the endless summer of youth*
> *As we searched for the distant shore"* . . .

As we finished, our eyes met, and she shed a tear.

"I tell you", she said with a warm and compassionate expression, "do you know how sometimes you hear a song, and the words somehow seem to describe exactly what you are going through at the time? That song was like that for me, and you have given me valuable perspective and insight on how to move forward, or as the " Doors " said, to "*Break on through to the other side*" . . .

"Yes, I know exactly what you mean", I said, "That is one of the most influential songs in my life"!

"Please do not misunderstand my intention or my generosity", she said softly, "but I have a very strong desire to give you my vacation. You have really provided me with some valuable healing, and in return, my soul tells me that somehow you can benefit from it more than I. Besides, it would be difficult for me to take the time off work"

"Thank-you very much", I stammered. "As a matter of fact, you are right. I am at a crucial cusp in life myself right now, and I need to find someone who can provide me with the knowledge and direction that I need to "*break on through*".

"When I was in college, I went to Tibet and studied for some time, and it was a very valuable learning experience for me. Maybe you can find what you are looking for there?" she offered.

So we exchanged telephone numbers, and she gave me her vacation voucher.

We talked about various things for a while, and rose to leave. I thanked her again, and she graced me with an affectionate hug, and a kiss on the cheek.

Wow, so I was going to Tibet! I hurried home and had dinner, and called the number on the voucher to make arrangements to leave the next day. That night I slept restfully, and I seemed to remember having some dreams in the middle of the night, but they were restful and normal, unlike the disturbing ones from the previous night.

I arrived at the airport in Lhasa, and stepped out into cool mountain air. I successfully passed through customs, and was immediately approached by an industrious looking young man, who offered his services in broken English as a cabby. I told him that I came to Tibet to seek knowledge, and he smiled and beckoned me to his cab, which was in fact an ancient, but serviceable 1962 De-Soto.

We drove to the town of Xigaze, (which is pronounced *Shigatse)*, and the cab driver took my fare, and directed me to a local tavern. He told me that, if I was lucky, and exhibited an appropriately respectful attitude, that I would find a helpful guide. I tipped and thanked him, and walked toward the bar.

It was a clear cold night, and the moon was shining brightly. It cast a brilliant glow to everything in its light, but also produced harsh, mysterious shadows. As I went into the tavern and walked up to the mahogany bar, there was a spearmint taste in my mouth, which was slightly distracting, as I was doing my best to exhibit a respectful and confident attitude.

The attitude must have been convincing however, because the bartender approached me and asked me what I wanted *in Tibetan.* Not wanting to blow my cover, I asked for a Josta Cola, thinking the name sounded almost Tibetan.
(For some reason I had been craving a Josta for the past few days, like I had almost got one when I was really thirsty, but then was denied.)

He looked at me quizzically, (much as a scientist would look at a slow rat who could not quite seem to grasp the fact that if it figured out the maze, that it would find a reward of a piece of cheese at the end), and put a pewter mug of warm goats milk in front of me.

I had the strangest sense of Deja` Vu, and every time I get that feeling that strongly, I get the taste of *mint* in my mouth. When I was a kid, I spent the best summer of my life at my uncle's ranch near Lake Tahoe on the California side of the border. A creek ran through the property, and when I went exploring there, I found to my instant delight that lush *spearmint* plants grew along its banks. All you had to do is get near them, and you could smell the pleasantly pungent aroma instantly and intensely. It was there that I had the most intense fccling of Déjà Vu that I had ever experienced, and so the *mint* aroma was firmly imbedded in my memory.

As I was sipping the frothy liquid, another individual walked in. It was dark in the saloon, so I could not make out details from that distance, but as the figure approached, I discovered that he looked awfully familiar, like somebody that I had seen at a bowling alley or library once. As he came up to the bar and sat down, however, I noticed that the stranger looked *exactly like me*, but he was *black*!

He asked the bartender for an astoJ soda in what sounded like a mid-western kind of Arkansas type of Australian accent. The balding pudgy barkeep looked at him, much the way that a bartender would look at a foreigner, and set a pewter mug of warm goat's milk down in front of him. He must have sensed my stare, because he slowly faced me and our eyes locked.

He approached me, his face a mirror expression of bewilderment and disbelief that I was feeling. The whole room got strangely quiet for a moment. The barkeep looked around nervously, decided it was time to distract himself (!), and put a record of some soothing (Indian?, Hindu?, Bohemian?) music on to an old fashioned phono-graph. It sounded a little tinny, but the quality of the strangely calming music offset this fact.

As I stood up to introduce myself, I experienced a fleeting *mint* taste, and offered my hand. He told me his name was nerraD, and that he had come to Tibet seeking enlightenment.

After the initial shock wore off, we settled into a quiet conversation about Aborigine pygmies. nerraD cleared his throat, much as a French spy would clear *his* throat just before divulging some secret information to his accomplice, and whispered that it was time that we went out for a smoke.

As we arose and walked toward a side door, we were being followed by the suspicious gaze of a dark stranger at the bar. I felt his gaze, and it made me uncomfortable (what was I getting myself into?), but nerraD did not seem to notice.

As we walked out into the sinister moonlight, he took a package of lemaC cigarettes out of his shirt pocket, much the same way somebody would take a pack of *Marlboros* out of *their* shirt pocket, and took two out.

He offered me one, and, placing his in his mouth, deftly flipped his silver lighter open with one hand, gave me a light, and then lit his own. He put the lighter back in his pants pocket, and then thrust his hand into the pocket of his pea-green trench coat. (*Mint?*)

He fished about in his pocket, and produced a dirty, greasy

piece of folded paper that was held together with at least *three different kinds* of tape.

"This valuable map was given to me by my great-great uncles twice removed cousin." (He never came back a third time . . .)

"On it are the cryptically encoded directions and maps to the esteemed Monks which live on a foreboding and inaccessible east wall in the Kunlun Mountain range".

(Local legend has it that there are Esteemed Monks who live there that must be truly wise and powerful, for they never come down for food or supplies from an area that is barren and desolate) . . .

So I said, "Awesome, but where did you get that cool trench coat?!"

"It is a secret", was all he said.

He tucked the map carefully away, and we extinguished our lemaC's, much like someone would extinguish a *Winston*, and walked back to the bar.

When we walked back in the room, I saw a group of tarnished looking mice (*mint!*) that were lined up and patiently awaiting their tarnish removing ointment. As we sat down, the dark man who had watched us suspiciously earlier approached us, much as a private in the English Army would approach two other privates which are in the same war, but in a *different company*, and sat down.

He introduced himself very formally, giving his full name, rank, and serial number, "ecurB nairB ydnaG, private, 9591712".

Then he proceeded to remove the clever disguise which he was wearing, whereupon we discovered that he was, in fact, a jolly and enthusiastic Aborigine Pygmy!

We bought him a mug of warm goat's milk, and he was so overjoyed at our generosity that he insisted on giving each of us a gift. (It is local custom that when a gift is received, one of equal or more value must be offered in return.)

To me he gave a *blue* glass jar of salve. He then gave nerraD a miniature goat that he explained was a very rare species that secretes the salve which is in my *blue* jar.

We both felt slightly jarred, but not so much that we spilled any milk.

"Guard these gifts well, and you might find that they will prove to be much more valuable and useful than you realize", he said in his little pygmy voice, which sounded so small in our big ears.

So we drank and told amusing anecdotes, and eventually we got around to discussing the cryptic map. ecurB asked to see it, much the way a teacher will ask to see a complicated trigonometry problem, for assistance, and to our delight, was able to de-cipher it!

Then, as the golden sunlight created by the rising sun crested the crusty edge of the Crest-fallen mountains, we knew that we had to finish the pie crust which we had ordered (that's what they eat there for their morning meal), and proceed to gather the supplies that we would need for our dangerous journey into the remote ranges of the Kunlun Mountains.

It was crisp, bright, and cold as we trod through the iron red dirt toward the dark and foreboding foothills. I was feeling quite jovial and optimistic, and I noticed that there was a dark beauty to our surroundings, much as a caterpillar would find beauty in the ugly skin of its chrysalis just before emerging as an adult butterfly.

"I know that we are on a dangerous and difficult journey, nerraD, but I believe that if we have confidence and perseverance, that we will be rewarded handsomely", I said, optimistically. Being somewhat of a pessimist, he replied,

"Shaw, and monkeys could fly out of my butt-hole too.........."

He choked hard on the last word, much as a fat slob would choke on the last morsel of food at a Vienna sausage eating contest, and his eyes got as big as saucers: because, at that precise moment in time, three very rare and exotic Tibetan

Flying Monkeys did just that! (Careful what you wish for, Jimmy . . .) Can you just imagine the look of shock and surprise that my face wore at that time, will you? (Did you ever get in front of a mirror and practice bizarre facial expressions that are designed to convey certain and specific feeling or intentions? Yeah, me too . . .)

He was very nervous and upset at this time, as you can well imagine, so we took a small break in a *hollow* hollow.

After he cleaned (!) and composed himself as best as he could under the circumstances, we nibbled on some left-over pie crust, even though it was well past breakfast time. (Local custom has it that it is *bad juju* to allow your pie crust to get overly crustated before you consume it…)

Finally the moon had appeared from behind the cloud which had been obscuring it, and by its pale frosty light we could clearly discern the steep precipitous path which beckoned us onward toward a fate which we knew not, much the way that a race- track would beckon a struggling runner running in the *Caledonian Marathon* to squeeze that last ounce of energy out of his tortured legs.

The scene was bizarrely surreal and dream-like as we watched huge crystalline snowflakes shatter against the step-edges of the slippery granite path which we were carefully navigating.

Anyway, to make a short story long, after a precisely predestined amount of time, we arrived at a high summit. (Did you say summit?)

We observed a small but orderly camp in a deep bowl nestled in the wind-torn eastern wall of a sheer peak.

As we wearily approached the sight I beheld two well-weathered tents which had snuggled betwixt them a large and rather tarnished silver tea pot. (I keep tasting *mint*!)

As we approached a mouse that was rather large and tarnished himself popped his head up out of the tea pot and announced visitors with a shrill ear-splitting squeak. After that he seemed quite disoriented and didn't say too much because, he lived in-between two-in-tents, he had not laid his little mousy eyes on another soul besides the inhabitants in-tents since the Mad Hatter's tea-party in Wonderland, and, mice can't talk.

Two Wise Old Monks emerged from the tents and contemplated us quietly, (much the way that God would contemplate a strange and intelligent new life form which He had just created), wearing serious, but benign expressions.

They appeared ancient, but their alert posture and the intensely penetrating look of their inquisitive gaze belied wisdom, power, and a certain silent certainty.

Gesturing us to sit with them at the fire, the Monk which had emerged first from the first tent asked, in *our own* language,

"You have undertaken a very long and perilous journey to grace us with your humble presence. What is it that you seek?"

"I am searching for the meaning of Death", nerraD said with vehemence, and just a touch of relish.

"And I am in fact seeking to gain enlightenment on just the opposite of that-I would like to acquire some understanding concerning the meaning of life", I said with humble respect, and just a touch of awe. (Aw, shucks John boy, you shouldn't have)

The second Monk which had emerged second from the second tent said, looking at us with his intensely penetrating stare, and just a touch of pity,

"We have made great sacrifices in our lives, and have worked long and suffered many great hardships for our wisdom, and deem it very valuable indeed. What do you have to offer in trade for our wisdom?

We looked at each other in depressed confusion, to have come so far and lack one final thing to obtain our much needed enlightenment, much the way that two rare tropical plants who suddenly found themselves in the middle of an arid desert would regard each other . . .

I had a sudden Idea - I took nerraD aside and whispered to him for a moment, and we agreed on an experimental plan of proceeding with the procedure of these proceedings. We broke our huddle, and returned to the Monks, each of us offering a small gift. The first Monk held the *blue* jar which I had given him up so that it would be justly illuminated by the frosty moonlight, and examined it carefully.

"This is a most worthy item indeed", he exclaimed in his large Monk voice, which sounded even larger in my small ear.

"With this valuable creamy alabaster ointment, I can *finally* polish my prized antique oriental ornamental silver tea pot. In addition, I can provide my prized antique mouse which resides therein with some long awaited relief by removing the tarnish from *his* coat. (Local legend has it that, although mice do not speak, it is widely believed that an accumulation of tarnish on their coats causes chafing, itching, and discomfort, and can in fact lead to *arsenic syndrome* if allowed to progress without treatment . . .)

The second Monk's reaction was even twice as intense at the offering which he had received, as he exclaimed happily that with the miniature goat's secretions, they could harvest enough of the alabaster ointment to last them a lifetime.

While Tweedle-Dee and nerraD retired to the second tent, (which was, in fact, water-repellent *(mint?)*), Tweedle-Dum led me to the first tent, which looked a bit more wind-blown and worn, and we went inside.

"My son, the meaning of life is that it is *precisely* and exactly that which you expect it to be. In other words, when you see the Cheshire Cat, he will vanish down to his famous and ludicrous big-kitty grin because of your belief and expectation that *that* is what is *meant to happen*. You see life, in all of its miraculous and amazingly expanding reality has contained within itself *infinite* (no boundaries) possibilities and it, like the delicate and fragrant rose, unfold into an ugly and stunted sight if the dirt is poor, and it does not get the proper nourishment, care, and light that it requires to achieve it's potential."

"If, on the other hand, there is nourishing soil, and it is cared for with the proper care and good treatment that it deserves, receiving even an occasional caress, admiring look, and encouraging phrase, it will unfold into a beautiful and aromatic blossom, which is what every little rose-bud and child genuinely desires and deserves."

The first Monk who emerged first from the first tent then looked at me with a sober expression and said,

"I have great knowledge and understanding about the vast enormity of the universe and the intricate and complex laws which govern all life, and these *qualities* give me great **POWER**. By that very **POWER** which is vested in me, I hereby place a special aura of *healing magic* around the wonderful and creative gifts which you lovingly construct from your wonderful and colorful materials, starting with the necklace and bracelet which you made last Thursday for your nephew, Bruce Gandy Jr.

Tell him that by wearing them with *humbleness* and respect, by being courteous and kind to EVERYONE, but especially to his family, that if he meditates[1] on the vast enormity of everything, (there is truly *much more* to the overall picture than meets the eye!), that he will be proportionally rewarded with success, happiness, wisdom, and long life.

These blessings will be multiplied even further if he has the patience to be nice to people *even though they are being mean,* because we realize that people often act thusly to have the satisfaction of manipulating us to have a negative reaction, thereby joining them in their **misery**. If we choose to react in this positive manner, it catches them off guard, and they are surprised and secretly feel guilty and are jealous of *our* ability to rise above their petty worldliness, thereby ***losing*** while we are ***winning***!

Later on that evening, we dined on barbecued Tibetan Flying Monkey, and joined in friendly and companionable conversation around the fireside.

The Monks told us of their poverty-stricken childhood, and how the Dali Lama had taken them under his wing at put them on the difficult road to enlightenment.

We left by the dim light of dawn feeling a lot wiser and a bit ill. (You try eating barbecued Tibetan flying monkey the day before a hike!)

While we were descending, I suddenly remembered where the Flying Monkeys had come from, and wretched violently over the edge of the cliff.

It did not seem to bother nerraD, however, and as I watched him scale down the precipitous path toward a fate which was somehow a bit more certain, I couldn't help but think that he was also approaching a crucial cusp in his life. I felt certain that he had learned what he needed to *break on through* in a glorious fashion. I felt a bond of brotherhood to this cosmic "twin" of mine, much as a 16th century Eskimo would feel bonded to a long lost brother which he had just discovered existed, and shared some whale-fat with.

As we approached the bottom, nerraD shared with me what he had learned, which paradoxically[2], turned out to be a mirror image to the things that I had learned.

At that point in time, I saw a bright flash of light, and a voice inside my head told me that nerraD lived in a different dimension, and that he was being returned there because he had gone out for milk for the evening meal three days ago, and had only come to my dimension so that we could fulfill our destinies jointly.

I suddenly lapsed into a deep trance, and the next thing that I knew, I was sleeping in my bed.

I awoke to the comforting sound[3] of my family arriving for Christmas.

I arose, stretched, and went into the living-room. Beneath the tree I saw a wondrous sight: It was a Polyphonic Strato-

Various, with a note from Santa congratulating me on my success, much the way that a President would congratulate a long-distance runner who had just won the Caledonian Marathon, achieved the rank of General in the English Army, and received a Master's Degree for an informative new study involving rats, mazes, cheese, and patient, positive conditioning!

So I picked up my beautiful *brand new* Strato-Various guitar, and proceeded to play a meaningful, moving, and healing version of "The Doors" song: "*Break on through* - *Break, Break, Break, Break, Break, Break, Break, Break, Break*!"

1 meditation-do this in bed before you go to sleep at night- relax, close your eyes, and imagine that you are floating.

2 paradox (ical, ically)- a statement or proposition that seems self-contradictory or absurd but in reality expresses a possible truth.

3 sound- an audible vibration which is detected by the *tympanic membrane* (ear drum) and passed along to the brain via the *auditory nerve* with a little help from tiny bones known as the malleus, incus, and stapes, terms that in Latin are translated as "the hammer, anvil, and stirrup".

This story is dedicated to Bruce Gandy Junior. RIP

The Soul: Illustrated

energy entwined

in existentialism

earthen clay enshrined

ex-is-ten-tial-ism: noun

Philosophy: a modern philosophical movement stressing the importance of personal experience and responsibility and the demands that they make on the individual, who is seen as a free agent in a deterministic and seemingly meaningless universe.

I believe that our earthly "shell" is animated by a spirit, or soul; and this is energy.

"In physics, energy is a property of objects which can be transferred to other objects or converted into different forms" Kittel, Charles; Kroemer, Herbert (1980-01-15). Thermal Physics. Macmillan

And since it seems that energy can be created nor destroyed, to me that means that this spirit has always been here in some form, doing something . . .

I'm Weary

~In loving memory of Michael Schmall~

Life goes on, hurry up!
Got places to go-
don't be alarmed,
don't get a bustle in your hedgerow

Work hard, live fast, and pay your dues,
and then you're laid low
You can't deny
you've always had a choice
of *where you will go*

Get up, get out,
hey what ya' doin' in your bed?
Kids are cryin', they got no shoes,
ya gotta keep them fed

Doin' too much dope,
ya gonna disconnect your head
So just keep on pushin' your luck,
you're gonna wind up
(weary, weary)

Flash, knock, I showed up
at your door yesterday-
(Why'd ya have to be so weary?)
I was standing there,
trying to think
of something to say
(How'd ya let yourself get so dreary?)

I was just hoping that somehow,
we could find a way-
(I tried to smile, but ya got so teary)
But when I noticed you were cryin',
I just had to turn away

(Ya gonna spend the rest of your life bein' WEARY)

So I packed my bags and hopped aboard
a north-bound train
And as I rode up
through the Colorado rain

I shed a tear myself
for causing so much pain
My, but it did feel good
to be on the move again!

I rode that train all the way,
to the end of the line-
Stepped off in Montana
to fresh air, and the pungent
scent of pine

It had always been
a secret ambition of mine:
standing in the moonlight,
waiting for
the planets to *align*

And as I felt the power,
surging through my veins
The **ENORMITY** of it all
was such exquisite pain!

Letting go of what I'd lost,
and grasping what I'd gained
After all that I've been through,
it's a wonder I'm still sane!

So as you wander through
the tangled web of life,
fear ye
All the troubles that
try to confound you
yearly

Try to see the good in the bad,
and
don't stay in one place *too long*,
Or you're gonna wind up
weary

This poem seemed to be prophetic, as a short while after I wrote it, my Brother-in-law, Michael Schmall, who married my sister Sara, moved his family to Montana. He passed away shortly after that in a motorcycle accident.

Endlessly Endless

the waves of the sea

never begin, never end

lapping endless shores

Winds of Change

floating on the breeze

getting better all the time

here come winds of change

Where am I?

I live on the earth

actually *existing*

in-between what's seen

The Crest

Golden sunlight
shines upon
opening bud,
breaking dawn

Filtering colors
for our view
warm and vibrant,
and richly hued

So begins
a brand-new day
teaching us
a better way

But we must also
do our part
to seek the path
that draws our heart

For, there is a way
which seems right to man
but in the end, is
only evil plans

The inexorable flow
and ebb of tide;
'tis a precariously balanced
tiger we ride

Black and white
good and bad
yin and yang,
happy and sad

And in the mix
we will discover
that we must learn
to interact with each other

The path we choose
right or wrong,
is meant to be
a complex song

Yet simplicity
is also present;
to acknowledge this
is presently pleasant!

To live for the moment
on the crest of a wave~
while one thing is lost,
something is saved . . .

Shades of Grey

This short poem was written NOW,
an experiment of prose~
something designed to capture how
I felt from my feet to my nose

You see, I am driven to write,
and this energy forces me to:
try as I may, try as I might,
do things the way that I do!

It occurs to me that people say:
that things are "white", or "black",
but I say that all things have a way
of over-lapping back

Upon themselves, creating, as it were,
shades of grey, so it seems
Quite often there is in the stir,
much more to the picture.

~ In dreams~

I have seen the truth,
of my sub-conscious mind
Currently, and in my youth;
the lines
breathe and *unwind*

Many of these words create
while I am sleeping
Some of the best ones emanate
during times of *weeping*

These words are a gift, and a curse!
If you sense a rift,
and see a hearse-
don't look too closely
at the face
or too morosely,
nor with *distaste*

For the lines thereon
might be *mine*
or, they might be
yours

As things begin to unravel,
in the other universe
they pour
into
the black-hole
of the mind, which
is universal, yet single

As with concepts which
are difficult, at best
to describe with
mere words

You see, the thoughts
meander and mingle.
At first glance,
it may look
absurd,

BUT, there is
madness
to my method!

These overlapping Shades of Grey,
have overtaken my grey matter:
and if you read between the lines,
you'll decide I'm as mad as
The Hatter!

On the other hand, you may choose,
to believe that I AM the hat ~
In which case,
I have come to the conclusion
that I am all three. . .

On my birthday in 2015, which was April 20, I was still in my addiction. I wanted to be clear-headed, so I gave myself ten days clean; from April 15-25. I went into the Yuba County Library on my birthday, and sat and completed this poem.

The Angels Use Brushes

~For my dad, who gave inspiration for this~

Angelic strokes
across the sky-
unknowing, uncaring,
a man in the street does not notice.

These heavenly brushes,
moistened with rain,
and dipped in moonlight
drizzle with luminosity

Amazing hues
blossom in the empyrean
while the Cherubim and Seraphim
admire their art

God Himself looks on
with an approving nod;
reflecting on the many reactions
pouring in from the Saints

Another blush-filled filled sky
went un-noticed by the troubled man.
But a child, innocent and wondering
sees the chagrined expression,

and says a small prayer.
The heavens are awash in celestial hues.
The trees clap their hands,
while the average man looks on in wonder

Dinner and a Bike...

Biographical

My friend Steve Green has a house
that is brown all around, but many
southwestern shades inside.
There's gold, Kokopelli, and more green . . .

His wife Sally doesn't dally, but she does like
Dilly Bars from Dairy Queen.
(She really knows how to make the scene
groovy when guests come to call . . .)

But here's something that I really liked:
after a savory dinner,
and coffee,
I got a bike ~

Sally's sister Myphon
likes making muffins,
and other lovin' stuff
from the oven . . .

And you would almost think it a sin,
when you hear the
silky *smooth* dulcet tones
from her magic mandolin-

So, one way that I know
that I am winner
(and a very eccentric sort)
is that I got Bike and a Dinner!
(Think I'll start a new sport)

Torrent

A wave of emotion, washed over me
like the dappled colors
of the leaves on the trees

It pinpointed me to: a moment in time...
which cannot be relived

So I Enfolded the impression
into my soul
I wept bitterly,
and it made me whole

I felt as lf
in an oil portrait
a poignant epiphany
in time,
that made me rhyme

The greens, oranges, and astonishing red
have slipped the feeling into my head
and made part of me, think instead

that I might in fact relive this moment,
as a reminiscent memory holiday
So I embraced the moment,
while my spirit leaped
a thousand years

Time to Write~

streaming back *behind*

time will roll on *forever*

now is a good time

Phoenix

bird calls, pine cone falls

sudden flame consumes them both

new life then springs up

Eternal Flame

spiritual flame

sparks fly; embers igniting

a glow in my soul

To Measure the Rhyme of Frozen Time

Frozen sunlight filters through
a lovely leafy lattice
the sun is rising, and the time is due
to exercise the practice
of the value of
these precious moments,
and the spaces
in-between

I long to experience things,
that are golden, new, and serene
Exotic, exact, and expressive
art is my medicine

it never tells lies
but sometimes it pries
into the bizarre
and obscene

corners of your mind
where you may find
hidden, *secret* things

It leads me to obscure places,
that might surely bewilder some folk
so untie your laces, tighten your braces,
and follow the smoldering smoke

Which will at first, might,
seem thick and concentrated
much like a beam of cloudy light,
Or quicksand, illuminated

Then suddenly dissipated,
drifting away in the wind
disconcertingly liberated,
both spinning and un-spinned

All the while breaking apart,
then falling together again
feeling emotion, deep in your heart
so sensual, it feels like sin

A curiously concocted waterfall
of the new and the old;
the thermal rise, then sudden fall,
of a tale repeatedly told

While falling I had a distinct desire
to take flight on sturdy wings
as close as I dare, to the ball of fire
what serenity this would bring!

Then once in flight,
my mind conjured up
two weirdly wonderful wishes:

The first was to be completely free,
the second, to live like the fishes
swimming with porpoise, in the sea
dining on plankton, delicious!

I then had three visions
won'drous, fair, and grand:

First I saw the division
between
the ocean, and the sand

The second was
the line separating
Earth Mother, and her air

The third drew me in
to outer space
won't you follow me there?

Out in the void, I slipped into
a state of hale hibernation

In this state of sleep,
while slumbering deep
I had four *dreams*
that gave me a keen, and
elusive sense of elation

I dreamed about:
the way things ARE,
the way things WERE,
the way things COULD BE, and
the way things SHOULD BE

I was tucked inside
a cosmic kaleidoscope, and
as I looked at the seams,
it seemed as if

everything was subtly shifting
just like the dunes of sand-
Father Time is slowly sifting
these realities through
his heavy hand

And once these grains of truth
pass all the way through
from what MIGHT BE
to: what IS

They are then IMMUTABLE
frozen forever,
locked into
Histories'
ABYSS

The original title was,

"To Measure the Weight and Rhyme of the Frozen Grains of Time".

In Chapter three of my biography, I mentioned that I checked myself into the Heritage Oaks Mental Hospital. It is there that I was working on three poems, and felt that I needed to finish them before I could be released. Those three were the culmination of this, as I discovered that they all fit together . . .

Marry Sleeping Mary?

Once upon a knight-time
in the valley of the sleeping,
a princess dressed in white
was trembling and weeping

~

She was mourning the loss of her
true love,
Prince of Avon-Lee
In her bed, she turned and tossed
in torment and misery

~

Sleep would not come to her,
but neither would open eyes
Her thoughts were foggy and blurred,
in a twisted turmoil of her own demise

~

Her prince it seems had left her,
some thirteen years before
Leaving her bereft,
and always wanting *more*

~

than the tattered memory
of the love that they had exchanged;
and the dreams that she, in her mind,
constantly re-arranged

~

Though she lay there turning,
linens in disarray
thoughts and memories burning
until that fateful day

~

when she woke to the sound
of the brook,
babbling as it turned
Arising, she looked around,
and this is what she learned:
- ~ -

She saw her handsome prince,
whose vision was doubling
and she took his hand,
(the stream beside still bubbling)
~
She asked, "What could be troubling?"
So the other took a stand
and whisking her away,
on a steed, sleek and black

~
To a place that was in back
of the places she lived before
in lives too numerous to count
~
And as he took the oar,
she measured the amount
of the tears that she had shed
for they made a river,
that led back to her bed,
where she was delivered
~
And, fully awakening now,
the dream slipped away like smoke.
The princess wondered how
she had earned the bloke,
that lie beside her sleeping
(but she was no longer weeping)

Haiku (sea)

thin sardines swimming

of course, you have to be slim

to fit in the tin

Bloody Waters

hungry piranha

so many razor sharp teeth

eating me alive

To Help Feed the Young

a mother eagle

her sharp talons clutch *my* catch,

I cut the line

Autumn's Slow Decay

Autumn coloured leaves

drifting to a sleepy ground

slowly decaying

The Birth of Earth

worth of the earth's birth

can obviously be seen

by its Providence

Currently Electric

lightning from the sky

the tree exclaims, "this is my

current atmosphere"

Newly Olden

Dedicated to my brother Daniel

I went back to my old street,
the place I learned to walk
The breakfast nook with padded seats
in front, the jagged rock

In back I saw a spotted cat
that looked so much like Fred
I had to wipe my eyes, and that,
made me feel instead-

Remember the time when you picked me up
lost, coming home from school?
You dried my tears, and quelled my fears,
and rocked me, wrapped in wool

I went back to my old home
the place I learned to walk
Rules were set in place, to hone
and undo the stubborn lock

There to make me reach:
for the stars, and beyond
To lead me to a distant beach,
and smell a fragrant frond

Peeling back the years, I saw,
in my cloudy thoughts
the conflict I had with the law,
and the freedoms that I bought

I went back to my old school,
the place we used to laugh
but the paint was peeling,
and I got this feeling

like waves upon a raft
on the sea of life,
it's constant flow
and ebb of tide

The timing's rife
for doing what you know;
to be part of the *lingering past*,
but willing to onward go

A wise man once said,
"You can never go back",
but I think that
that long-drawn
conclusion is,

conjecture, at best
a matter of perception
If one thing is valued,
above all the rest,
it will overcome:
the deception of not
living in the past,
but learning, nonetheless

Because, after all
is said and done,
more is *said* than *done*,
and LESS is MORE,
more or less . . .

Adam's (Simple) Apple

An apple fell on Isaac's head
and as it fell, he surely said,
"This is not the fruit
the snake proffered"

Man's soul to dilute,
perfection, deferred

Concluding that
mass was the cause;
core of Earth Mother,
invisible claws

Earlier structures
built of stone
endless conjecture
history, hewn

Then came the *dawn*
of the age of reason,
conclusions drawn:
Heresy, Treason!

The stones were laid
the stage was set
the serpent bade,
and made his bet

He took his place
souls lured away,
from God's perfect grace
a deadly relay

(With the possibility of:
eternal dismay)

The apple rolled
and then was crushed
The bottle was filled,
there fell a hush

Smiles all around
the jug of cider
population bound
to swell ever wider

Encompassing
the whole
of a singular thought

Structure: indole

Dignity: sought
Vanity: wrought
Integrity: bought
Insanity: taught!

Towing the line
so tense and taut
then; unwinding
It is now

that one is finding
that things are
vastly complex
yet all so simple

These thoughts have
but,
to be popped,
like pimples
on the face of a giant,
his steely gaze steady,
resolve reliant,
as his flock dissolves

This nation's compliant
while we grok,
yet still spar,
for a place on the land;
weaker species
beware!

Survival of the fittest
Darwin's creed
in health, and in sickness
we must succeed

To be seen and heard
locked indeed
in between the third
and fourth sphere

Lies a harsh mistress:
the moon, abjectly listless,-
yet spinning in light

the sinner whistles
in preparation to right
the wrongs that ain't left yet
the seal was tight

but the ground was wet
and, in mid-flight
caught in the net
causing slow decay

The agent, O2
to aid entropy,
for me and you
You see?

I do

Grok- a term by Robert Heinlein from the book, “Stranger in a Strange Land”, it means to understand something completely.

Good Things are Gonna Come

Dedicated to Dr. Gerstein

When you do wrong
it can be a sad song
seemingly endlessly drawn

out to seem
that even in dreams
you feel like you're only a pawn

In the chess game of life
there will be strife,
but be in a cheerful way!

For these hurdles are
to make you look farther
than just that scene
or that day

Rollin and tumblin`
shouting then mumblin'
something about the blues

Two wrongs ain't right,
so fight the good fight
when it comes to payin' your dues

Think outside the bubble
and then when trouble
comes your way, you could:

See it as learning
for your heart is burning
to set things to
be as they should

When things are their worst
and your dyin' of thirst
that's when you should strive to
DO RIGHT!

Then when you leave
and your kin are bereaved,
(from this shell taking flight)

No one really knows
where exactly we go
when we go from this flesh
to the air;
but good things will
come to you, I know,
when you stay out of
darkness' snare

I am a living example
so please don't trample
on my beliefs or my ways

For when you look deep
and don't try to keep:
anger, or unforgiving

You will feel the ways
of the sunlight's rays
of bathing the space,
and the living

So if you are smart
please do your part:
instead of taking, try giving!

Wanna get high?

Griffon Vulture, at

thirty seven thousand feet,

soars above the clouds

Frequent Flier Miles

what bird flies farthest?

Arctic Tern can fly to the

moon and back three times!

Stone Bird

Archaeopteryx

an extinct primitive bird

only fossil now

Entropy

Listing and falling and fading away
living too fast is the American way
but I find that the more time that passes today
that the quicker I go, and
the more that I know
I just stubbed my toe
they need me below,
and sometimes *time* seems to go *slow*

Wanting and longing and hoping to find
running fast-forward, but feeling behind
But I know that I have to get back to the grind
'cause I need more money
I can't find my honey
my nose is runny
and I feel kinda' funny
I've GOT to go somewhere and unwind

Quickening, thickening, feeling *intrigue*,
wanting to be "IN", but OUT of my league
Got to keep pruning, but getting fatigued
I just can't stay awake
and here comes a quake
I just stepped on a rake
and fell in the lake
Now I'm washed up and besieged!

Sometimes I just want to dance,
caught up in romance
just need one more chance,
but met with so much resistance

Searching and asking, but still feeling lost
sometimes we don't seem to realize the cost
of their wheeling and dealing
my senses are reeling
the cycle is wheeling
and I can't shake this feeling
that,

yeah, time's going way too fast!

Entropy: noun
Thermodynamics.

a. **(on a macroscopic scale) a function of thermodynamic variables, as temperature, pressure, or composition, that is a measure of the energy that is not available for work during a thermodynamic process. A closed system evolves toward a state of maximum entropy.**
b. **(in statistical mechanics) a measure of the randomness of the microscopic constituents of a thermodynamic system.** ***Symbol:*** **S. 2. (in data transmission and information theory) a measure of the loss of information in a transmitted signal or message. 3. (in cosmology) a hypothetical tendency for the universe to attain a state of maximum homogeneity in which all matter is at a uniform temperature. (heat death)**

Words ARE Powerful!

the structure of ice

can be manipulated

by the *spoken word*

The Seed of Tomorrow

sack of seeds in hand

in search of moist, fertile ground

planting *tomorrow*

Mother's Cupboard

here is your brother

or it could be another

fed by earth mother

Damn It!

The damn has burst
the water is flowing
do what I durst
we must be going

to the higher land
where the sun's still shining
this is NOT what I had planned
but there is no time for whining

Because below, is H2O,
it is to the HILLS
we must quickly go

Up where the scent
of Pine fills my senses
(My money's all spent
from these circumstances)

Although, it seems though,
the flow is unwanted
soon flowers will grow
proud and undaunted

in places where they
were unseen before
but, with no delay,
I must man the oar

To save the poor chickens
I must get them or,
I'll get a good licken'
that will leave ME sore

There a'floatin', & cackling
unnerved at their plight
from their grave, I'm unshackling
but they put up a fight!

Wings frantically flapping,
and wild, scared eyes
the waters a' slapping
terrifying: our demise!

Now, I've gathered them up,
so re-luc-tant-ly
into the small dingy,
they, and me

It is now that I see,
that I surely find,
that our fowl have got ME
in a foul state of mind

Oh my, I need *dry*,
ground to unwind
(sometimes I wish I
could just *rewind*)

Happy Mother's Day

Mothers always seem to know
the very best way for us to go
They teach, they toil
we reach, she's loyal

They give, we take
and make mistakes
We bump our head,
she tucks us in bed

But sometimes you *don't do*
what she so patiently says,
this always leads to trouble!
So, listen and DO what she says,
and you'd better do it,
on the double!

Thanks for teaching
me how to live
to *love*, to *prosper,*
and how to give

I don't know how
to show my thanks, *for sure*
but, this I know:
your reward is secure!

Your loving son, Darren

< : - D ~

Dead Air ~ Dark Light

~A session to question deception~

Languorous liquid darkness
Infused with a soft, silky glow
growing is my dynamic spark
and this feeling is all that I know

I wonder what is out there;
thinking mutely, why art we here?
but the only reply,
was the beat of a heart
all the rest was dead air

Twisting and rolling,
my sphere was cajoling
me into a perpetual lull
a lot of sleeping,
a bit of weeping,
and then I felt a *pull*

I was rudely plucked
from my comfy dark warmth,
into the cold noisy light
In my lung, an air bubble formed,
I wailed with all my might!
(My mind already furiously forming
a notion of wrong and what's right)

Then I was snugly swaddled,
comforted, and fed
I considered my role model,
and listened intently
to all that was said

Grasping, I quickly learned to do:
all that I endeavored.
At times I felt sick
my thoughts were churning;
I quickly became more clever

Rolling and tumbling,
I bumped my head
on the leg of a kitchen table
I wanted to run, but walked instead
becoming more awkwardly stable

Seeking and yearning,
I found myself learning
in my new found world
I experienced many
wonderful things
as my ***reality*** unfurled

I was running,
then I found myself sunning,
amidst a field of rye
I considered the birds,
their manner stunning,
and wondered:
how it would feel to fly?

Soaring then, in a vivid dream,
my rapid eye-movements, implying
that things were not as they seemed,
but, I was really flying!

Gazing below, to a valley, *lush*,
dream-wind tousling my hair
the moon-lit air was cool to the touch
I was maneuvering without a care

Detecting a glint in my field of sight,
a reflection of a snowflakes' facet
it was then that I thought I might
embrace the ice, and ask it:

"If we are merely actors,
performing our lines,
why do some roles
seem more varied?"

Others seem to have
been born blind,
and, in time, they tarry-
Travelling down a rocky road,
'tis a heavy load they carry

But I learned not to judge
for I found that a grudge
held on to holds me back,
onto this ledge which I'm
precariously poised
yet, complete wisdom I lack
I drifted then, to the valley below
in an attempt to gauge the balance
between the air, here and there,
and to practice the talent

Of this delicate dance
in which we are entwined
caught up in this *romance*
woven into my mind
Is the future, already written
or do we own the choices?
By life's joy, I am smitten
as I join in the many voices

crying out to be heard
amidst the toil and clatter.
Would you think it absurd,
or would it really even matter?

That, my fancy, attentive friend,
would depend on one's perception;
is this the beginning of the end,
or is it a clever deception?

I work for an independent polling firm conduction surveys over the phone. Of the many ways which calls can be coded, like busy and disconnected, is “dead air”. This is the inspiration for this poem.

Angel's Faith ~ Holy Spirit Come

Chapter V

The Holy Spirit is a palpable catalyst; the binding agent that connects, convicts, and communicates with us constantly, to those who acknowledge and are receptive. This "Force" or "Energy" is all around us at all times, whether we interact with it or not. And of course I am certain that there are times that we DO have interaction, or protection from The Holy Spirit without realizing it.

I was born with some mental challenges including ADHD, obsessive compulsive disorder, bipolar type I, and Tourette's syndrome. This complex combination of mental factors has basically hardwired me to be a thrill seeker who can't pay attention to what he's doing. Making my life quite exciting, but the downfall is that I tend to be extremely accident prone, and have looked death in the face three times. So, my average mental state these days is one of a variable spontaneity that conforms roughly to my schedule or obligatory items that happen to be on my agenda.

One of the many reasons that I enjoy living in Sacramento, California is because of the Capitol's many valuable and rich resources that are available there for not only disabled people, but any number of other sub-sets that you can imagine, AA/NA, etc.
One such program is known as "the Ripple Effect". Their philosophy is that, by helping the lunatic fringe, or mentally disabled sub-set of the homeless population, that these good deeds will spread out like a ripple into the community.

Their services include a drop-in day center that provides lunch, basic first aid, access to the internet, and to other community services. I have received a lot of assistance, help, counselling, and moral support from the wonderful staff there.

I was riding my bike to the RT train station to head home one evening after having taken care of some obligations downtown. The setting sun lent a warm, maroon back glow to the downtown buildings. There was a pungent aroma of wet leaves in the air. I entered the park that surrounds the Sutter Fort near 28th and J streets, and rode past the white walls of the fort, the quacking duck pond, and the Indian Museum. Cutting across to where The Ripple Effect is located above the Church, the thought crossed my mind that I might stop in and say hello, and let them all know how well I was doing, and how much I had appreciated their help in my time of need. But I decided to keep going toward home, as it was already after their normal business times, and I was hungry.

Then, it occurred to me that I was being "pulled" in that direction, and I have learned to become sensitive to this pull. As I turned into the alley way to the entrance of the program, I could see that the sign was no longer there. Like so many things in life, they come and go like so many birds mimicking the scattered nature of my thoughts.

I looked toward the fenced in area where clients could store their bikes and carts, and the small playground for the children. Kneeling there on a dirty blanket was a pregnant homeless woman, with her head wrapped in a cloth cover, and a rosary clutched in her hand. She was rocking and praying in a haunting sing-song that did something weird and wonderful to my spirit. As I approached, her head rose and she looked at me like . . .she *knew me*. Tears were streaming down her grime-tracked cheeks, and on her face an expression that reflected rapture. Looking up at me with startlingly clear blue eyes, she asked me, "Are you the angel that I was praying for?"

By this time, this came to me as no surprise, nor did I find my response ironic, "Well, I don't know. What *exactly* were you praying for?"

She proceeded to explain that she was at her wits end, that she had faith, but was looking for some type of help or confirmation, anything that would aid her in her time of desperate need. She said that she did not feel like there was relief in sight from any source. She had just recently married, but her husband was not keeping his end of the bargain.

"You see, he is addicted to heroin, and he told me that my love was the only thing that could save him. But still, he makes no effort at all to do anything toward abstaining from this horrible habit. And it is killing him, and tearing us apart! I just don't know if I should stay with him or not!"

So I looked up and gave thanks, clasped her trembling hand, and prayed. In my past I would have been a bit more ambivalent about praying for something requiring a specific prayer, but I have since garnered a more positive and lasting connection to The Spirit, and am never at a loss for the proper words.

So as The Spirit guided my words, my prayer of supplication for my sister in Christ flowed out like the river for which the city is named.

Like so many other areas of my life, when I "Let go and let God", things go a lot smoother!

After we prayed, she stood up and pierced me with those intense azure eyes, and a sober expression that indicated genuine gratitude for my compassionate help. I gently reminded her that it was not me, but rather the spirit working *~through me~,* to come to her aid, and that all thanks should be directed above. She looked up, gave thanks, and gave the sign of the cross in a way that had more meaning for me *right then* than it ever had.

"I will heed your advice and consider everything, my tender one. You do not realize how much you have restored my faith in mankind and our creator", she exclaimed warmly, in her endearing sing-song language.

I turned to leave, my tears conveying and confirming the joy that one experiences from being touched by the spirit, and the knowledge that through that spirit I am not only more capable of performing that which He would have of me, but also the warm feeling of having been able to help provide sustenance and faith for a flagging believer.

So, if you are somewhere doing something and you get a sudden urge to do something else, *heed the pull of the spirit*

I turned to gaze at her as I left, and called out,

"My name is Darren, and you and your husband will be in my daily prayers. What are your names?"

"My husband is Isaiah, and I am Angel. Thank-you so much, and may God Bless You"

When you feel the spirit, heed the call, and you will be proportionally rewarded. In my opinion, one purpose for existence is to interact with each other in a mutually beneficial manner; positive networking.

Making the World Safer!

"The safety of the people shall be the highest law" Marcus Tullius Cicero Roman-Statesman 106-43 BC

I love everything that you do,
for this helps us in so many ways.
As I step into the morning dew,
I know I'll be safer today-

We have been encouraged,
with the help you provide.
Me and my entourage,
can take even more pride-

in the lives that we lead.
Though we made some mistakes,
you have sowed the seeds,
and gave us a fair shake.

The guidance that you gave
caused us to be less alarmed;
our sanity, you saved,
giving us *power* for less harm.

Thank-you
for all that you do!

Here in Sacramento, CA there is an organization called Harm Reduction Services. They provide free supplies for addicts. I truly believe that they have prevented a lot of spread of diseases. They have also prevented deaths through education, and providing free antidotes for heroin overdoses, which are common, and have caused a lot of fatalities which could have been and are now being prevented. They have provided me with help with food, transportation, and moral support, and I for one am very grateful. Thanks!

You are NOT the center

A brief dissertation on the history of reality, philosophy, and our collective consciousness

Now is the acceptable time; for TODAY is just the perfect day for contemplation:

Is it raining?

to think about where you are, they are, WE are, as a nation

are we gaining

on the TRUE meaning of *everything*?

Now is the only time that matters, the past is gone and the future has yet to arrive. But yet, although we cannot with one-hundred percent accuracy predict what is going to happen, we can *speculate*. But even that is a slippery and dangerous term, for is that not one of the many complex factors that caused the demise of the stock market? Sane, grown men plummeted to their death! (I am speaking of the infamous stock market crash that occurred here in The United States in October of 1929)

Descarte, who is dubbed as the father of modern western philosophy, was a French scientist, philosopher, and mathematician. Born March 31, 1596 and deceased on February 11, 1650. Rene Descartes said, "Cogito ergo sum" which translates from the Latin to, "I think, therefore, I am". Along with this self-consciousness came a self-awareness AND a self-centeredness.

In the time of Nicolaus Copernicas, (2/19/1473-5/24/1543), a renaissance mathematician and astronomer who formulated a model of the universe that placed the Sun rather than the Earth at the center of the universe, men believed that the earth, for what it's worth, was the center of EVERYTHING. How ego-centric is that? He was the first scientist to imply that our system was heliocentric, with the earth and planets revolving around the sun.

He was afraid to publish these findings, however, because they conflicted with the beliefs of the Roman Catholic Church.

Moving forward, more about US, A thought: This great country was founded on the premise that we, THE PEOPLE, are all endowed with certain inalienable God given rights to pursue what we choose, so long as it does not interfere with others, or cause harm.

How does that measure up today? In a time when there seems to be more division than unity, more hate than love, higher prices and less money, even less value for the "money" that does exist, more strife and less life!

Perhaps you do not believe that one person has enough power to cause real change, but look at what one humble man did? He put EVERYBODY ahead of Himself, and cared so very deeply for us all that He came, and gave His very life. If we follow his example, we may not be able to change the world, but we can make it a better place.

If you have a good attitude, it will affect your immediate environment. This ripple effect will create many overlapping shades of gray, which contains darkness and light. As these concentric circles merge, it will slowly, then more urgently, get brighter, until the darkness is consumed.

And this will be one of an infinite cycle which we, as organic blobs of cells, chemicals, and flesh, could not even fathom to comprehend a *tenth* of, but yet, we are intrinsically connected to; therein lies the mystery; it is neither bad or good, it just **IS**.

The Bridge

I awoke from a vision
when I was quite young
as a matter of fact,
life had just begun

I wriggled, crept
crawled and slept
bittersweet were
the tears that I wept

Slipping into manhood
around the age of thirteen,
I looked and felt good
but was still between:

That age of magic,
and this of reason
abrupt and tragic,
this change of seasons

Then I emerged,
as if from a cage
the lines had merged,
I was now middle aged!

I pushed and pulled
utilizing my powers
escaping a lull;
a late blooming flower

Those days of youth,
became fleeting flashes
then came the truth:
ashes to ashes

I was then transformed
as if from a trance;
I'd torn *through* the fabric
of happenstance

Breaking through
to the other side,
I found no shadows
in which to hide

And as I approached
with apprehension and awe,
A Magnificent Light
was all that I saw

I tried, in vain
to discern the sight
and, as I paused
in mid-flight

I saw visions
of heaven, and hell
but it was too early
for me to tell

As then back
to the earth I fell . . .

I awoke from a vision
when I was quite young
as a matter of fact,
life had just begun

Tre` Realites'

Try, sigh, cull

Things are not
as they appear,
objects are nearer
than they look
in the mirror

I'm not the person
I used to be
I'm not you, and
you're not me

Everything seems
to be spinning faster
Are we in control,
or in for disaster?

There's got to be
something in between
fall, oh!
through the cracks,
and you'll see what I mean

Try to see things
from a different angle;
an alternate corner
of your triangle

(pause on the edge,
and let your legs dangle)

And, when you get there,
call out your decree
we'll meet in the middle

and then you will see
That I am YOU,
and you are ME
We are three,
I AM, you, and me

To be, or not to be:

Thrice we be free

"I am he as you are he as you are me and we are all together", John Lennon, from "The Walrus" From the 1967 Beatles album, "Magical Mystery Tour"

Tre: a French term for three

cull: verb (used with object)
1) to choose, select; pick
2) to gather the choice things or parts from
3) to gather; pluck

thrice: adverb
1. Three times, as in succession; on three occasions or in three ways.
2. in threefold quantity or degree.
3. Very; extremely.

Apogee

"Love recognizes no barriers. It jumps hurdles, leaps fences, penetrates walls to arrive at its destination full of hope" Maya Angelou

I plan to reach my apogee
around age of one-hundred & three
It is then that I will reach the height,
of discerning between wrong and right

I awoke at the age of three plus fifty,
from a spell: deceptive and shifty!
Existing in a deluded fiction,
caused by dastardly addiction

We can fly pretty high
here in this sphere,
but as we so *eagerly* try,
things become more clear-

That there is much more to this,
than meets the senses!
As we prepare for the abyss,
for which there are no defenses-

We will break through,
and become imbued:
with our *original form*,
and then we'll swarm

Some to the dark,
which will devour their spark-
others into the light,
having learned to do right

Our time here is so brief;
the conflict of living-
If you are seeking relief,
you must be forgiving!

For if you keep anger inside,
there will be nowhere to hide-
as you enter the light,
your burden will be dark as night

So as you live, learn love-
and you will be completed;
Soaring on the wings of a dove,
as the darkness is defeated!

If you find this to be a *mystery*,
try not to be dissuaded;
for you cannot re-write history-
So enter the light, and be elated!

Irish

A Biographical Limerick Suite

{These stanza titles are Gaelic words for the seven days of the week}

Dé Luain
An Irish lad from Reno,
wanted, but to grow:
in body and mind,
his life was designed,
to grasp the oar and *row!*

Dé Máirt
He grew up fast, and strong,
and before too long,
he was laughing and skipping,
slipping and tripping
Then things began to go wrong

Dé Céadaoin
By the fire's light, he envisioned:
her lurid indecision
Inviting her in,
she got under his skin
So began this callous collision

Déardaoin
For her careless caress he yearned,
but he slowly, subtly learned:
That her love was electric,
then things got hectic!
Tumultuous tide, it turned,
being badly burned,
yet, to her, he returned

Dé hAoine
She took him for a ride,
from her lure, he could not hide
He began to weep,
while losing sleep
The path to her door was wide,
feeling lost inside-
crystal shard collide

Dé Sathairn
Then one day, rising early,
feeling sprite and squirrely;
for she had slipped away,
in a mysterious way~
Sucked into a twisting swirly

Dé Domhnaigh
You see, life is like a river,
the current makes him quiver
But Irish broke through,
and you can too!
(A lass, she's gone *forever*)

When I wrote this today, I could not help but notice its seven stanzas (I count EVERYTHING), so I wanted to include seven Gaelic words, and decided on the days of the week.

There's a great little song in Irish (based on a folktale) called De`Luain, De`Mairt, in which a crippled man called Donal Bocht Cam (Poor, Twisted Donal) rescues a group of fairies from the monotony of singing Monday, Tuesday, Monday, Tuesday in Irish over and over by supplying the Irish word for Wednesday.

The fairies reward Donal by removing the hump from his back

and sending him on his way healthy and sound (not a typical result of encounters with Irish fairies, which tend, on the whole, to be rather unpleasant creatures!).

You may never encounter a group of fairies stuck on repeat, but, if you're learning Irish (or thinking about learning it), it's always useful to know the days of the week (and how to use them properly).

First, the basics. If you simply need to recite the days of the week, here is what you would say:

De Luain (Jay LOO-in): Monday
De Mairt (Jay march): Tuesday
De Cadaoin (Jay KAY-deen): Wednesday
Deardaoin (JAY-ar-deen): Thursday
De hAoine (Jay HEEN-yeh): Friday
De Sathairn (Jay SA-ha-rin): Saturday
De Domhnaigh (Jay DOH-nee): Sunday

Brother Badger March 17th, 2017

Happy St. Patrick's Day!

Space/Time Fabric Softener

The fabric of space/time is curled
alas:
as *that moment* unfurled;
if you are clever,
and it's your endeavor,
you can certainly change the world!

I Must Confess . . .

I cherish me Irish kin,
who live in a world of sin;
but when we confess,
He cleans up our mess,
and in the end, we will win!

Green Goddess

I covered my lover in green
she looked really keen
So, covered in clover,
I said, "roll on over,
and join in an intimate scene"!

Emerald Isle

Come visit the Emerald Isle,
that is filled with Irish style
I snuck away,
to stay for the day,
but ended up there for a while!

Castellany Clouds

Fluffy
cotton-candy clouds
super-imposed upon:
the imperial empyrean

Head in the vapour,
observer, gaper

Feet on the ground,
hanging around,
earth mother;
(no others;
silence abounds)

Feeling physically fit,
my mind scribing a *writ,*
a bit of worthy wit

Thirsty thoughts
entwined,
I don't mind:
I find, as I unwind,

~~~

I'll go my own way,
respite for the day
Pondering
her way

and to
this moment,

~

be consigned . . .
~~~

Logos Fotia` (Word of Fire)

I release my writing
in words of flame,
that fly a mile high

Flickering, fighting
none the same
into the "bye and bye"

A spectacular sighting
which *cannot* be named,
asking the question: why?

Ashes alighting,
on this moment, framed
as I scribe "logos" on the sky

Passions igniting;
fighting to tame
feelings I cannot hide

I strive to write
the wrongs I've named,
to feel whole inside

Deep purple night;
tinted shades of shame,
now I lay me down to cry

But, until I die,
In *hope* will I abide.
Flickering flames, collide!

My Poetry Inventions:

Fifteen, twenty-five, and thirty beat poems, and ukiah/haikus
This section is dedicated to Emily Rose, Abigail, and Sydney

I, am, hear

15 beat poem for Emily Rose

I

I am

I am here

I am here now

I am here now *dream*

With my OCD, I wanted to do a scheme of 1_2_3_4_5 syllables, so I did. Now, on 11/23, I am experimenting with the last line. Another change, still looking for the perfect last line . . .11/24 write. 22-2. bow 12/15 learn, 12/19, I decided to leave it blank, as I was considering all of the words that could go there, BE is the strongest, I overloaded! Can I write a poem with a blank in it? (rhetorical) December 28 dream ~

His Star

15 beat poem for Emily Rose

*

A
New star
Rising in
The east when He
Beheld His chosen

Floating Home

15 beat poem for Emily Rose

As
I look
down at my
body, I feel
like I'm going home

Breathe

A 25 beat poem: om for Sydney

I
snuck in
to your mind
don't look behind
try to look ahead
instead of back
let out slack
relax
breathe

om, pronounced ohm
noun: om; plural noun: oms
a mystic syllable, considered the most sacred mantra in Hinduism and Tibetan Buddhism. It appears at the beginning and end of most Sanskrit recitations, prayers, and texts.

That which is NOT hidden

A 25 beat poem for Sydney

You
try to
hide, but I
saw what you did
It could not be hid
from my keen eye
You can't hide
now from
me

Based on my idea of a symmetrical poem which has 1, then 2-3-4-5-4-3-2-1 syllables. I like the balance~

Rager!

A 25 beat poem for Sydney

You
are in
my mind, yet
I'll make a bet,
a little wager:
turn the pager,
the rager
that is
me

Ordered Chaos

30 beat poem for Abigail

Where
are we
with the way
things are in this
chaotic world
today there seems to
be more evil
than good but
we can
be

Sine of the Times

30 beat poem for Abigail

I
exist
in a sine
wave of the sun
from which all things come
e v e n t u a l l y
everything
will return
to its
eye

Spaces in-between

30 beat poem for Abigail

I
live in
the world
but I exist
in the time between
the spaces where you
can see the light
that exudes
from the
ki

Ki, or Chi - the circulating life energy that in Chinese philosophy is thought to be inherent in all things; in traditional Chinese medicine the balance of negative and positive forms in the body is believed to be essential for good health

The Other Side

A haiku/ukiah experiment

I long to look at
the other side of the coin
to see what is there

lifting with my fingernail,
suddenly I see:
that I DONT see all that's there!

With my OCD, (obsessive compulsive disorder), I flip things around. To my delight, I discovered that haiku backwards is not only a word, (in the native American language it means 'deep valley', which also seemed appropriate), but also the name of a city here in California!

Up, DOWN, and up again?

An ukiah-haiku experiment

Climbing up the rocky hill,
I just saw a snake!
And rolled all the way back down.

When I got back up
I thought I might try again,
snake-bite kit in hand~

¡Solo Baila! (Just Dance)

"Welcome to the human comagedy" Brother Badger

When this comedy
twists and turns around
and becomes a tragedy,
don't put on a frown-

~just dance!~

It really doesn't matter
if there is music playing.
I know you will be gladder,
with the style you're displaying.

Just relax, and close your eyes,
and feel the rhythm of the beat.
They will be surprised
at the way that you compete-

as you resist their friction,
by the smile on your face.
The "drama", their addiction,
will put them in their place!

I went to a gala circus,
a mischief-maker started hating.
The clouds overhead were cirrus,
their wispy tendrils translating:

to an even atmosphere,
and a lazy, tranquil day.
Beneath the clouds, the sky was clear,
as the music began to play.

So I looked him in the eyes,
and I started dancing.
Then, to our sincere surprise,
the horses started prancing!

Then a hyena joined in,
laughing at that hater's plight;
which made the monkeys begin,
to fling feces, to his utter fright!

The seal slapped his approval,
then deftly balanced a ball.
We shouted for his removal,
as night began to fall.

Then everyone started grooving,
to the festive sounds they heard.
To the "outcast", we were moving,
who looked and felt absurd.

We descended upon the stranger,
who by now, was cryin';
his eyes conveying *danger,*
as we threw him to the lion!

Who proceeded to gobble him whole,
then dance a gay jig of his own.
Spectacular was his role,
as he courageously danced alone.

So, when a "hater" gives you lip,
do what you know is right:
Smile and move your hips,
and just dance off into the night!

Poor Frogs Wish

I'm just a poor frog

living in a dry creek bed

I wish it would rain

Catch Me if You Can!

Salamandering

along the pebbled creek bed

catch me if you can!

Feeling Froggy?

Mississippi mud

brother frog says to tadpole,

"you'll jump too, morrow"

Sanzaru (Three Monkeys)

~Mizaru~

I will *speak* no evil,
for to utter such
might show my human flaw,
(by then I've said too much).

But I learn
to bite my tongue,
to starve my ear,
and feed my lung.

~Iwazaru~

I will *hear* no evil,
but there's evil *all around!*
It is the type which,
does not *make a sound.*

Be sorely fearful of
the fowler and the snare.
In the deep of quiet night,
pay heed and be aware.

~Kikazaru~

I will *see* no evil,
for its ungodly sight
For, to see, and not believe,
is a precarious plight!

So as I fine tune my senses,
this epiphany encounters me:
As the road unwinds behind,
in front is not *all that I see.*
Content that I can be:
Here.
Real.
Now.

The three mystical monkeys (as they are sometimes called) are named the sanzaru. Their names are Mizaru, Iwazaru and Kikazaru. In Japanese language, ~san~ means three and ~saru~ means monkey.

You probably have already seen three wise monkeys in miniature or in picture where one covers his ears, the other covers his mouth and the last one covers his eyes. But do you know what it means? In western countries, its our habit to see them as decorative objects without speaking of their true signification. Of course, they are far from only decorative objects.

Its hard to date the first appearance of the three wise monkeys. They have been brought into Buddhism by a monk in the 7th century. According to the legend, this monk, while he was travelling, was escorted by a monkey. His name was Xuanzang, one of the most important translators of Buddhist texts in China. He left China for India when he realized that it was time to seek more Buddhist texts to bring to China.

Nevertheless, he's not the one who invented the three wise monkeys, but the one who made them known. The first traces lead us to the wisdom of Confucius (between the 4th and 11st century BC). Several legends assume that those three monkeys came from Japanese Koshins belief. They are based on the idea that, in every human being, there are three wicked worms, the Sanshi, which, every sixty days leave our body to report on our sins to a superior entity, Ten-Tei. Still, its tough to make the difference between legend and reality.

Moreover, one of the oldest known representations of those three monkeys is on the front of the Tshogu temple in Nikko, Japan. Would they come from Japan then? It is possible.

In Japanese language, ~san~ means three and ~saru~ means monkey. Time passing, ~saru~ becomes ~zaru~, giving birth to sanzaru.

Yet, ~zaru~ is also a negative form, that we could translate to ~not to~ So the common admitted meaning, ~not see~, ~not hear~, and ~not speak~ could come from a Japanese play on words. Besides, in Japanese culture, monkey is supposed to ward off evils.

Meaning of these three wise monkeys: Those three wise monkeys are supposed to represent a way not to feel evil. The common sense is: not to see anything, not to hear anything and not to say anything. But can it really be that simple?
To me, such a philosophy can hardly be reduced to this only sentence.

Through those monkeys, let's have another approach: not to see the evil, not to hear the evil and not to say evil things. That can be explained by the idea that, each time we see something bad, a part of it enters into our body. Similarly, hearing the evil or speaking of it makes a part of us turning into evil. Those three little monkeys would be a call to refuse the evil in our life. This point of view stays questionable; should we close our eyes on the evil? Should we shut up when someone says bad things?

Looking into the past, such thoughts have led to horrible acts it's certain that ignoring the evil won't make it disappear. Would it be the original meaning of those three monkeys ? Probably not, but we are getting close.

Interpretation of these three mystical ~not to~:

More and more people give a new explanation, each a little bit more subtle. Instead of not to see anything or not to see the evil, the message could be the following one: I see everything but I look to nothing, I hear everything but I listen to nothing, I think of nothing to become everything.

In other words, I would be conscious of everything happening around me but I would choose not to let it reach me. According to me, we can see an idea more simple: to think before speaking. We have to learn how to think by ourselves, not to listen to anyone and not to always trust our pretending-full-view-eyes. But everyone should have his/her own interpretation of the three wise monkeys. Then, what is yours? To sum up, those monkeys have a really particular meaning. May we learn to see them more as a life philosophy than as decorative objects?

Source: Wikipedia

Steve's Green Reign

In loving memory of Steve Green

A very good man,
Steve Green was the name
of the flesh, he was granted
a life-time to claim

We celebrated his life,
a magnanimous man
leaving Sally, his wife;
all part of *His* plan

He suffered two strokes,
then was lucid again!
Just one of the spokes,
of *the wheel,* still in spin

A celebration was held,
the service was grand
Myphon rang the bell,
and thunder rolled
across the land!

~He let us know that he was there
by the
thunder-claps that filled the air~

The angels wept tears
that *quickened* the power
of the faith of the believers,
as a church bell rang the hour-

A man, sought after here,
his style and class we loved
But it became clear, that
he was ever meant for above

Myphon spoke a peaceful phrase
then struck a dulcet bell
When it rang a second time,
the angel's tears softly fell

~We *released* his spirit!~

The angels greeted him,
and wrapped him in
their love
that flowed into the raindrops
which then fell forcefully
from above

Although his flesh is gone,
to the earth we rescind;
his spirit and legacy live on
in sweet memories, and
the wind

Written after a magical service, Sunday, June 11, 2017
I met Steve when he was hosting "open mikes" at Java Retreat on Plumas Street, in Yuba City, California around June of 2000. He always did his best to promote whoever was performing, and really went out of his way to make you comfortable, and to enhance your performance as much as possible.

As time went on, we became close, and I was a friend of the family, which included his wife, Sally, and their son Zachary, or "Zack".

I had the pleasure of performing with them, and I have a very fond memory of playing "America", by Simon and Garfunkel. Steve had a great wit and a complex and varied sense of humor, and was always quick to jump in with a great one-liner.

The day of the celebration, I rode from Linda to Yuba City. The clouds rolled in, and for the service there was great rumbling and rain! Afterward, the sun came out . . . .

At one point in time, they invited me over for dinner, AND gave me a bicycle, as they had just bought a new one. I wrote a poem for it which you can find in this book titled "Dinner and a Bike", on page 80. We also enjoyed my Blackberry Chess cake that night; you can find the recipe on page 209.

Darren

June 16, 2017

Raining Blessings (Ladder Rain)

~For my Uncle A.J.~

I am so very blessed,
my cup runneth over
As I reach the crest,
I've come out from cover.

Into the sunlight,
bathing, sustaining;
to continue the fight,
no time for feigning!

Into the "fray",
is my direction;
I'll wrestle today,
but with discretion.

We must choose our battles,
and not waste resources;
try not to get rattled,
while *weaving* these forces.

For, there is much more,
than meets the eye
look for the door,
that's up in the sky.

A secret ladder,
climbs to its portal
a major matter,
vital to mortals.

Its rungs are a mystery,
to the average soul,
we're writing our history,
as we play these roles.

Shakespeare exclaimed,
"All the world is a stage".
The set is the same,
the wisdom, still sage

Some subjects climb,
others never will-
they have not the time,
noble cause to fulfill.

Slippery when wet,
hold on a bit tighter!
Let go and let,
God be your fighter!

"For vengeance is Mine",
sayeth The Lord
If you're so inclined,
those blessings will pour:

like Holy Rain
into your life;
easing the pain,
and calming the strife.

Why does it seem,
the unjust get reward;
while we, who dream,
die by the sword?

Take away the "S",
and you get "word",
this word is *finesse*.
Oh, have you heard-

The freedom bell,
ring out in the land?
As time will tell,
of The Master's plan.

Where two or more
gather reverently,
He reveals that door-
for the chosen to see.

So, if you are bound,
let your light shine!
For, those not found,
will be *left behind.*

It continually rains,
on the rich and the poor;
look not with disdain
on that hidden door.

For you will pass through,
when your faith is sustained.
So, whatever you do,
sing and dance when it rains!

I think I'll walk

A goofy Booby

calls to friends flying over,

"I think I'll just walk”

Bitty Berry

Bitty Berry is a fairy;
but he has no wings

He collects copper coins,
silver rings,
and other shiny things

Then strums a lute,
whose sound is mute,
because it has no strings

With ease
on the breeze
his melodic notes float
as to the mushrooms he sings!

Somewhenever, Time and Time Again

"A little nonsense now and then, is relished by the wisest men" Roald Dahl, author

To live, then die
seems so significant;
to experience "the high",
what more could you want?

We enter this mode
in a traumatic way.
This poem is an "Ode",
to ***ALL*** that has
led up to this day.

For *now* is the only
acceptable time;
yesterday was lonely,
tomorrow, sublime.

To ponder the enormity,
of "before", and "after".
Think not with enmity,
try a little laughter!

For this cosmic riddle
reeling for OUR pleasure;
if you think your part is *little,*
take a more
mature measure!

But, we must earn
our timely rewards,
we all must learn
that we cannot afford:

to approach *reality*
with *apathy,*
for what will be, will be.
Let your gift *unfold*,
and you will see:

That you reap what you sow!
And, if you work hard and well;
grasp ahold of the oar, and
~row~
and then
time, and space will tell . . .

what exactly will transpire,
when we do go from this *flesh;*
we'll go even higher,
space/time fabric enmeshed.

Knowing more,
feeling less.
Through the "door",
into somenothingness . . .

~Let your spirit roar!~

Into the great beyond
where obscure *secrets* are told;
and the inhabitants are fond,
of their *spiritual fold.*

Floating
aboding.
Hiding,
abiding.

Seeing,
being,
free~

"You have to get old because of the geometry of spacetime".Brian Cox, Forces of Nature

"But Einstein came along and took space and time out of the realm of stationary things and put them in the realm of relativity giving the onlooker dominion over time and space, because time and space are modes by which we think and not conditions in which we live". Dimitri Marianoff, Einstein: An Intimate Study of a Great Man

"Everything I do now was once an unremembered dream".
-Spoken by Dr. Perry after return from the chrysalis.
Don Murphy, EPOCH

My Tumultuous Life!

Chapter VI

I have been living at North Side Recovery for about a year now. Located in scenic Del Paso Heights, a suburb of Sacramento, California. It is owned by Bill and Patty, who are done with this career, and have worked hard to earn a peaceful retirement.

The whole property is on the market. This includes two more houses, and five two bedroom cottages out back. There are roses, gardens, wonderful shade trees, a hammock, and a lush green lawn.

Bill and Patty are good people, and throughout a thirty year span, have helped countless people come to live recovery, many of them still residents, friends, and neighbors.

The house manager, Bill G, is a very thoughtful, kind, and under-standing man who has overcome great obstacles to be in his current position. I would give my life for that man, is his worth to me AND mankind.

The house is older, but nice. There is a dorm, living-room, kitchen, office, and my room-mate Curt and my bedroom upstairs. There is gas for cooking, and plenty of utensils and kitchen gadgets for my gourmet cuisine style of cooking. There is a laundry room, with washer and dryer in the entry-way to downstairs, where there is one bedroom, and another dorm.

When I moved in, there were three mandatory meetings a week: Tuesday AA, Wednesday NA, and Thursday House meeting. Sean did the NA meeting, but when he left about August of 2016, it was very natural for me to fill in and take over.

Plus, it was not only very rewarding, but it gave me an opportunity to: polish my speaking skills, give me some more direction and structure, and learn to bond with my house mates in a setting that is conducive to growth and, therefore, a greater sense of self confidence, trust, and love between us all.

As time has gone on, all of the meetings have stopped, except for the house meeting, where Bill reminds us of the house rules, which are fairly standard.

Since I moved in, there has been a tremendous turnover in house managers and residents, and a lot of people who leave, end up improving, or otherwise, and come back for another stay.

The rules are very lax, and there is very little structure or program, as everything is in a constant state of flux chaos. Because of the un-balanced nature of the environment, I have really been challenged with learning what I call, "The finer art of social interaction under the most interestingly difficult circumstances". I have learned a whole lot there in what seems like a very short time!

There was a resident named Tim, who was watching TV loud. When I came in, I kindly asked him to turn it down, and he did, so I went to bed. Then he turned it up again, so I asked him again, and he ignored me. So, I reached down for the controller, and quick as a flash, he jumped up and socked me in the eye! Now, here is a very good example of my growth, and my ability to "rise above and beyond the call of duty". The old me, well, it would have been on and crackin', and I fear that there could have been very serious injury or death.

But, the *new me*, stood back, analyzed, and called the house manager, who was Doc at the time. He came immediately, and made sure the friction was over, for the time being.

The next morning, Bill asked me if Tim hit me, which I replied in the affirmative. Then he asked me if I fought back, to which I replied "no", and he told me that he was proud of me. And *He* told *Me* that He was Proud of Me! Do you know how good it is to hear that, after you have been struggling, toiling, and suffering? The icing on the cake.

Now, there is a new conflict: there are jealous bullies there, and it has escalated to the point that I am literally afraid to go home. I am working, stable, and have been clean and sober for fourteen months on April 4.

I do not feel that it is fair, but all of these things happen for a grand purpose for, if we can get a bare glimpse of this "Grand Performance", it is all written in The Good Book. Ecclesiastes chapter 3 states:

1 To every *thing there is* a season, and a time to every purpose under the heaven: 2 A time to be born, and a time to die; a time to plant, and a time to pluck up *that which is* planted; 3 A time to kill, and a time to heal; a time to break down, and a time to build up; 4 A time to weep, and a time to laugh; a time to mourn, and a time to dance; 5 A time to cast away stones, and a time to gather stones together; a time to embrace, and a time to refrain from embracing; 6 A time to get, and a time to lose; a time to keep, and a time to cast away; 7 A time to rend, and a time to sew; a time to keep silence, and a time to speak: 8 A time to love, and a time to hate; a time of war, and a time of peace.

So, to paraphrase, there is a time for Darren to be comfortable, and relax, and there is a time for great friction, which results in growth. Anything worth having is worth working hard for, the greater the extent of work, the greater the proportional blessings, or gain. I have been suffering from asthma, allergies, and breathing problems, and it is raining blessings. So, hallelujah, when it rains, it pours!

I am going to count my blessings, and thank The Good Lord, in His Infinite Wisdom, for blessing me so profusely, and giving me this opportunity to return love for hate. I actually had a talk with this individual and, being human, I detailed why he acted thusly, including things like jealousy and a deep-seated inferiority complex. I had had enough!

Well, things just escalated because I could not control my pride. But, the last thing that I told him, and have repeated many times since, is that I genuinely love him, and want him to succeed. This is one of the things that made him angriest, like he is possessed of a demon!

Ecclesiastes 3, continued: 9 What profit hath he that worketh in that wherein he laboureth? 10 I have seen the travail, which God hath given to the sons of men to be exercised in it. 11 He hath made every *thing* beautiful in his time: also he hath set the world in their heart, so that no man can find out the work that God maketh from the beginning to the end. 12 I know that *there is* no good in them, but for *a man* to rejoice, and to do good in his life. 13 And also that every man should eat and drink, and enjoy the good of all his labour, it *is* the gift of God. 14 I know that, whatsoever God doeth, it shall be forever: nothing can be put to it, nor any thing taken from it: and God doeth *it*, that *men* should fear before him. 15 That which hath been is now; and that which is to be hath already been; and God requireth that which is past. 16 And moreover I saw under the sun the place of judgment, *that* wickedness *was* there; and the place of righteousness, *that* iniquity *was* there. 17 I said in mine heart, God shall judge the righteous and the wicked: for *there is* a time there for every purpose and for every work.

You see what I am getting at here, when I look at these seemingly insurmountable elements in this light, they grow smaller.

18 I said in mine heart concerning the estate of the sons of men, that God might manifest them, and that they might see that they themselves are beasts. 19 For that which befalleth the sons of men befalleth beasts; even one thing befalleth them: as the one dieth, so dieth the other; yea, they have all one breath; so that a man hath no preeminence above a beast: for all *is* vanity. 20 All go unto one place; all are of the dust, and all turn to dust again. 21 Who knoweth the spirit of man that goeth upward, and the spirit of the beast that goeth downward to the earth? 22 Wherefore I perceive that *there is* nothing better, than that a man should rejoice in his own works; for that *is* his portion: for who shall bring him to see what shall be after him?

I do rejoice in my works, the fruits of my labors. I am happy, blessed, content (to an extent), learning, growing, and I have retained my youthful spontaneity and zest for life. And it is kindled even brighter now, for as I reinvent myself, I realize that I have been given many valuable gifts. And with that comes a great and unshakeable responsibility to live up to my potential.

I am ever indebted to: God, My Lord and Savior, Jesus Christ, The Power and communication of The Holy Spirit,
and to my loving family for instilling the good traits that I was raised with, like honor, integrity, honesty, courtesy, and an abounding wonder for the majesty and scope of this cosmic

dance; in which we are a bit more major players that we sometimes realize!

I would also like to thank the folks at CARES Community Clinic, for ongoing health and psychiatric care, therapy, dental (I have new teeth!), chiropractic help,
and a really great pharmacy.

I would like to extend my heartfelt appreciation to Bill and Patty, Nichole, Bill G, Doc, Shelly, Julia, Cappy, Christy, and anyone who has been part of the staff.

And, last but not least, to my friends at FanStory for giving me so much positive feedback- you are an integral part of this stage of my life, and you can all be proud of your accomplishments, your feedback, and your outstanding attitude.

To quote Roger Waters of Pink Floyd, in his honor and remembrance of past bass player Syd Barret:

"Shine On You Crazy Diamond"

Darren Gandy,

Survivor!

The Lord Is Good, All the Time!

Chapter VII

I am writing to let my readers know that God is good, he answers prayers, and sometimes you just have to be patient.

In chapter six, I talked about problems that I was having with bullies where I live at North Side Recovery.

Specifically, (names have been changed for courtesy and discretion), Dave and Ken moved in. Now, Dave is a tall, goofy kid who laughs a lot (loudly), is up-beat and bubbly. He, like me, is a type A outgoing and intense personality, and enjoys being the "class clown", having the spotlight.

Ken is a schizophrenic (not the only one there) who had a hard life growing up as an orphan in group homes, etc., including abuse of all kinds. He is a brilliant poet, so we connected right off the bat.

Then Dave got jealous, angry, and for some reason, my presence became threatening to him and got very hateful to me. One night Dave and Ken came out and proceeded to "tag team me", one making me angry and the other telling me that I was being disrespectful by raising my voice. This brought up an ocean of emotion from my sub-conscious memories of being small and bullied in school. I was terrified!

Dave was complaining that I was watching TV too late, and proceeded to turn the TV off. I had finally had enough, and I went back and knocked on the night man's door. He did not answer. Next, I called Bill G., who also was unavailable.

Out of options, and literally locked in my room with them jiggling the door knob, and taunting the way bullies do, I called the police.

The dispatcher said she would send someone, but called later (~!~) to say that they had been too busy.

Finally Cappy, the night man got up, and I told him what was happening.

Hopefully I am conveying the level of hostility in my environment, and how it was having a continuing and horrible effect on me.

The next morning, Bill G., the main house manager, got very angry with the situation, and told Ken that he had to pack and leave. He said, "I cannot have other tenants locked in their room, calling the Police"

But, things being the way they are, after the steam blew off, Ken stayed. I am glad that he did.

It was getting to the point that I was ready to go back to the hospital, or the streets, or anywhere else.

I was entering a state of deep and insidious depression, and was suffering from anxiety, a feeling of hopelessness, and my mind kept obsessing on these things, trying to find a solution.

Now, I have gotten reviews telling me that I "over" wrote this, but I am merely attempting, as desperately as the situation was, to find the *appropriate words* to *accurately describe* the complex and mixed up emotions that I was experiencing!
I believe I have done an acceptable job at this. Thanks for being patient, and reading on!

I am going to utilize scripture from the King James Version of the Holy Bible to help explain: This is from the Old Testament book of Proverbs, chapter three-

1 My son, forget not my law; but let thine heart keep my commandments:2 For length of days, and long life, and peace, shall they add to thee.3 Let not mercy and truth forsake thee: bind them about thy neck; write them upon the table of thine heart:4 So shalt thou find favour and good understanding in the sight of God and man.5 Trust in the LORD with all thine heart; and lean not unto thine own understanding.6 In all thy ways acknowledge him, and he shall direct thy paths.

If I just trusted Him to go before me, it would have saved a lot of needless worry. You see, I have been trying to do things "my way" for a long time, and old habits die hard. I prayed that Dave would leave; yet another subtle but obvious error on my part.

It says that we are to acknowledge Him "In all our ways", and He will direct our paths.

As someone who has experienced His Holy Spirit, AND human behavior, I have come to the realization that, while in "the flesh", we are incapable of "acknowledging Him" twenty-four hours a day, seven days a week.

So, we acknowledge Him when we can, and learn through trial, error, and to acknowledge Him more and more often, and with greater zeal and joy, because He is so good to me, all of the time.

Well, Dave came up to me and apologized last night. He patted me on the shoulder, shook my hand, and sincerely apologized for his behavior.

To balance the equation, and because it was the right thing to do, I followed suit, and we walked away having shaken on a mutual peace treaty.

And, one reason that he did this, as I discovered later, is because my room-mate, Curtis, told him that I was getting depressed and miserable.

He told him that I was fun to be around when I was at my best, and not in a hostile, unfriendly environment.

I am thankful, humbled, and my faith is not only sustained, but strengthened.

I am much more at ease, and have returned to my feelings of being at peace with God, my chaotic environment, my housemates, and myself.

Darren~ Monday, April 24, 2017

Mrs. Doubt's About Time

Twisting and turning, combining
entwining whining and squirming
My heart is yearning;
burning to be learning about
returning
to the *time before*
our fall from grace

We, The People,
the human race
quickening the pace
of this
blessedly forsaken place;
random disgrace

I'll make a wager,
a turn the pager
a "right" to "left" stage her

Stunning manner
of flying her banner
as Mr. Time ran her
image through *his* mind
(bump and grind)

It reminded *him* of the time
that he climbed
that tricky trellis, over
by Lake Ellis only to find:

other "fellas"
had the same game
in mind . . .

So he returned to
the "scene of the crime",
Justin Time
is *his* name,
and his claim to fame was his
insane flame blame game

Which came with:
strings attached;
while lighting a measured match
to be applied
in the wink of an eye
which was lost
with the cost
of the convoluted concussion!

The quick catalyst,
a vehicle for his
rushin' to the nearest
Optometrist for a
quick twist of the
Doctor's wrist,
then perhaps, a game of "whist"

If you get the *gist*
of the justice which
Justin times just right
to keep his left eye out
for the next Doubt about
how we fell, but
not to worry:
he won't tell . . .

Wanderful Thoughts (Daydreamer)

For my brother Bruce

I let my thoughts wander
away over yonder;
into the Milky Way

Galaxial fodder
as I grow fonder,
of its silky whey

Cosmic curds,
(this may sound absurd),
travel on parallel rays

Spinning to the middle,
and this is the riddle,
I must find how and why they decay

Where did they go,
I surely must know,
I must find out today
I need a reader, for I am their leader!

So if you see them,
tell them, "Please Stay"

"Of whom are you asking?",
I ask myself,
but alas, there is *no reply*

For the *other* is out,
out and about,
on that starry
curds and whey tide

~~~
~~~

Driven

For my sister, Sara

I am driven
it's a given
in the game
of give and take,
make no mistake:

That I have acquired
more than I desire!
Amassed a surplus
then put up a fuss

Data overload;
I've entered a mode
where I am casting off,
like a persistent cough-

That which hinders,
dodging the cinders
that seer and burn
it's high time to learn

The wise words of
my worthy wife
she gives substance
to my life.
Her silver hair is flowing,
she knows where she is going

I yearn to attain
her confidence-
you can see it in her eyes,
she abhors their lies

I feel the pain,
and the expense
of those moments,
lost;
and the value,
found

I've counted the cost;
now more, I abound!
I seek the lost,
to reveal the
love all around

If you will but
reach out,
you'll feel it too!
What it's *really* about,
that it *is* true-

That you are right
where you're meant to be.
Don't put up a fight,
let go, and be free!

To accomplish that,
of which you are
meant.
You're up to bat,
so don't get bent!

Mend your ways,
lengthen these days.
Eat healthy,
and be wealthy
in the things
despised by this world.

As our future
unfurls
you will find,
that your mind
is better than ever!

Jump in to life's river
that flows
as it goes,

Through the land:
of milk and honey.
And, as for money,
(which is, in fact NOT
the root of all evil),

But if you put *it* first,
then you're un-level.
Place everything in
its proper perspective~

And the future will bring:
a shiny objective
that will unfold
like a fragrant flower.

As has been told,
we possess the power
and with that hour, comes
more responsibility!

Where we are from,
where we can be.
Don't you see,
isn't it clear?

Freedom is free!
So, if you hold it dear
please do your part-

Look into your heart,
for today is the day
to embrace our
true identity

Hold fast to that truth,
we knew in our youth
Then we will see,
and truly succeed

To plant the seed
for an abundant future
Pull out the weeds
so the ground
can be nurtured

Grab hold of the reigns,
endure the pain
for suffering is,
but for a minute

Then, comes the gain
and,
when you are in it
you'll look
inside and out,
and see:

everything
in a brand-new light;
for that brief moment
all will be right!

Twisted Endzz

As I peruse my collection
of reflections
which I have elected to select

emanating from the
oceans of emotions
which are:

ebbing in my
mind's eye,
I ~ find,

while carefully unwinding
these neural pathways
to their source,

of course, my only
recourse
is to adopt the role of
"Thaumaturgist",

to attempt
to untangle
the many mangled
endzz.

But,
they resisted
to be untwisted,
and in fact, with a
pact of tact, enlisted
a resisted method of changing,
curiously, constantly rearranging.

Oh, how we
persisted!

How,
now, I detect
that they have
wound around
that which I have found:

An elusive gem of truth
that was planted in my youth;
forcefully faceted,
with sufficient heat
and pressure.

I am in the middle
of a little riddle
that seems as large
as a mental barge

which, in my *dreams*,
seems to have
many tenacious tentacles;

far-reaching implications
teaching these
elaborate equations.

Recreationally levered
endeavors,
a *fixture* in my mind
Fixed and mixed
with a clever mixture
of work, and play.

Today I find a *wary way*
to connect
However, as
IT
happens,

the ragged endzz
are overlappin',
trappin' the
slappin' synapses.

Injecting and
infecting
with a sustained dose of:

not necessarily
pleasure,
pain, or
particularly peculiar particles,

but rather a
palpable and
piercing personification of
self,

making
~me~
more intent
on the content
of the file
in my mind's eye
labeled,
"content".

Now I am entering
an arena in which
I am:

entirely
enthusiastically
entwined
with myself.

We are
free to
be three,

why,
"I",
"myself", and
"me".

We try,
die, then
fly . . .

~~~~~

~~~

~

Darren is Called

Chapter VIII

Hi. My name is Darren, and I found out at the age of seventeen that there is a lot more to life than partying and raising hell. (I turned out to be the only hell my mama ever raised) Not that I am a big hell raiser, I was actually blessed with a loving, caring, and nurturing family.

Born April 20, 1963 at Washoe Medical Center in Reno, NV. I have two older brothers (my immediate family), and a younger sister.

Bruce is four years older than me, Shawn two, and Sara is twelve years younger.

I had a magical childhood, I have lead an extravagant life, and I have enjoyed the best of both worlds, good and bad.

My first job was at a dump in Carson City, Nevada at the age of fifteen. I got paid cash under the table, and it instilled a good work attitude for future jobs. I collected recyclables, cleaned up discarded brick, and other various landfill duties.

My second job was at Village Inn Pancake House, in Rock Springs Wyoming. I was sixteen, and I learned to hustle pan flipping eggs, while the wheel was wrapped, and the harried waitresses were scrambling for their orders.

One of the most rewarding things about this job was learning to appreciate the finer art of cooking breakfast, and separating to beat the egg whites up fluffy to make the best pancake batter.

I was also be exposed to what was to be some of the most

valuable advice that I ever considered.

My Boss, Dennis, told me, "It is a good idea to come to the job with a professional attitude."

And this implies a lot of things; being prompt (at least fifteen minutes early), clean, with appropriate clothes, you don't gossip, steal, lie, or bear false witness, you pay your debts, and you strive to become part of the solution, not the problem.

But, he also added that it is a good idea to adopt this attitude in LIFE. And that advice just stuck.

Next, at the age of seventeen, I worked for Charles Brown and his loving wife, Ione, at Eugene's Pizza, in Green River, Wyoming. Here my duties were: making pizza dough, constructing mouth-watering pizzas, sub-sandwiches, and soups, maintaining the salad bar, and prep cooking.

Charles was a kind, patient boss, with a good attitude, and a compliment for everyone. He exhibited a sunny disposition that was immediately engaging.

One day he hosted a "Full Gospel Businessmen's Meeting", and invited me to grab a soda and take a break.

The first thing they did was pray, and give thanks for their many blessings. Some of the men were praying in a different language, and I wondered, but figured that it was some language that I had never heard.

Then they did some laying on of hands, and healing.
Now, I was quite skeptical when I saw a man was healed for having one leg longer than the other, I figured they were pulling my leg, pun intended.

Then they had an altar call. The man got up, and asked if "anyone" felt the need to ask Jesus into their life. I was a long-haired, pot and tobacco smoking kid, and I did NOT want anything to do with those Jesus freaks, or what appeared to me to be a phony presentation.

However, before I knew what was happening, something was pulling at my heart; some invisible strings seemed to be connected. As I reluctantly but undeniably stepped forward, I was crying. Now, I have always placed a great deal of value on this activity, and do it daily, but usually not in public, after the age of about eleven.

Looking back, I realize that the tears represented a couple of things: that I was in love with the world, but had to learn to leave these "earthly" pleasures behind; that I was being granted a huge gift of eternal life, which I had little comprehension as to the value, scope, and significance, and It was the end of innocence.

I Peter 2:9-10 states: 9 But ye are a chosen generation, a royal priesthood, an holy nation, a peculiar people; that ye should shew forth the praises of him who hath called you out of darkness into his marvelous light: 10 Which in time past *were* not a people, but *are* now the people of God: which had not obtained mercy, but now have obtained mercy.

So, I came to learn that *my name* was written in the Book Of Life before the foundation of the world. And, I am peculiar.

Now, my logical, scientific mind is screaming, "If this is all written, then are we mere robots?"

But, I have come to find out that the answer is resounding NO! We have been granted the choice of free will, and the most important thing to me is to fulfill the Great Commission, to *actively* seek where I can find those lost sheep, and gently lead them into, or *back into* the fold. It is literally as simple as that.

Now, it has not been easy, but I have come to find out that God has groomed me for His good purpose. He has blessed me abundantly, led, protected, and guided me *every step of the way.*

Even when I was doing wrong, or *especially* when I was doing wrong. He has amazingly and undeniably proven His existence to me *beyond any questionable doubt*, and I am so grateful.

The best way for me to explain this is with scripture.

John Chapter 10: 1 Verily, verily, I say unto you, He that entereth not by the door into the sheepfold, but climbeth up some other way, the same is a thief and a robber. 2 But he that entereth in by the door is the shepherd of the sheep. 3 To him the porter openeth; and the sheep hear his voice: and he calleth his own sheep by name, and leadeth them out. 4 And when he putteth forth his own sheep, he goeth before them, and the sheep follow him: for they know his voice. 5 And a stranger will they not follow, but will flee from him: for they know not the voice of strangers.

I am a preacher, philosopher, and poet, and these three P's work for the *good* in my life. I believe implicitly in The Good Book, for I know in my heart that God, who was wise enough to create all of the splendor of this magnificent world, and the heavens, and the vast galaxies, is faithful and just to have an *accurate* copy of His Word available to His followers.

I will claim Romans 8:28, which says: "And we know that all things work together for good to them that love God, to them who are the called according to *his* purpose."

There you have it. Not *some things*, not *good things*, and not *bad things*. All things. Furthermore, verses 29-31 are more evidence of my calling:

29 For whom he did foreknow, he also did predestinate *to be* conformed to the image of his Son, that he might be the firstborn among many brethren. 30 Moreover whom he did predestinate, them he also called: and whom he called, them he also justified: and whom he justified, them he also glorified. 31 What shall we then say to these things? If God *be* for us, who *can be* against us?

And yet, this is still just the beginning of this wonderful and exciting path which I have chosen.
Won't you consider following?

Revelation 3:20 Behold, I stand at the door, and knock: if any man hear my voice, and open the door, I will come in to him, and will sup with him, and he with me.

It is my prayer that this testimony is presented with a special blessing to all who read and hear, and I state this on April 23, 2017, being of a sound mind, in The Name Of Jesus Christ.

Diamond in the Rough

forming very slow

great heat and pressure below

there, a diamond grows

Emotional Eruption

sheer intensity

of poignant emotions

words are erupting

Fire and Ice

curling sheets of light

icy mountaintops on fire

empyreal glow

Fish Tale

fish out of water

feels the arid air, and says,

"I'm out of my league"

Friendly Flames

The days are shorter

Chilly winds invade my nights

warm flames console me

Grateful Grapes

Gargantuan Grapes

laden with sparkling dew drops

reflections of earth

The Greatest Dad in the World

Chapter IX

"Honour thy father and thy mother: that thy days may be long upon the land which the LORD thy God giveth thee" Exodus 20:12

Now, most people like to claim that they have the world's greatest dad, and they are certainly entitled. I may not have the "world's greatest", but I am blessed to have a father that loved me when I was growing up, and instilled in me the old-school values that were carefully reinforced. These include, but are not limited to:

1. ~Respect
2. ~~Integrity
3. ~~~Courtesy
4. ~~~~Honor
5. ~~~~~Honesty,

and a deep and insatiable curiosity and love for the many splendors of life itself. I remain "rich" in these qualities.

Born in Martinez, California in 1936. He married my mother, and I am the third of his three sons in my immediate family.

I have a lot of fond memories growing up in Concord and Martinez CA.; Rock Springs and Green River, Wyoming.

One night he had gotten a promotion at work, and was excited. When he got home, he greeted my mother with a bottle of, let's call it "Martinellis' sparkling apple cider", to be politically correct. She was busy with housework, my brother's homework, etc. and did not have time to join in his celebration. So, we sat at the table across from one another, and proceeded to drink that magnum of "cider", while cheering with mounting gusto to: George Washington, and Abraham Lincoln.

By the time we were done, I found myself singing, laughing, and splashing bath water on my mother, who was angrily bathing me and putting me to bed!

I am very fortunate to have been introduced to singing at an early age. From about the age of four, my dad would line us boys up by the amplifier to entertain and delight guests with Christmas carols. Now, singing and performing comes very naturally to me.

When I was about seven years old, my father had a bad accident where he worked; a large dryer fell, and when he deflected, it crushed his spine.

At one point in time, my mother was a nurse at Mount Diablo Hospital, in Concord. My father was there in traction, and I went in for an inguinal hernia surgery. So, my mom came and got me in a wheelchair, and I went and had ice cream with my dad.

They wanted to do "exploratory" surgery, and by that time he had been talking to a chiropractor, and he had had enough! So, he came home and was laid up in bed for a while.

It was the beginning of training in one of my many talents, massage therapy. I had to learn how to rub his back to ease the muscle spasms. It was difficult at first and in the process, it was necessary to apply great pressure with my elbows to key pressure points.

We had some great bonding times then, as he would tell me stories of his childhood, and I would share my thoughts about this and many other subjects while enjoying the finer art of sharing fine cheeses with more "Martinellis' ". His Chiropractor got him back on his feet, and he has maintained a relationship with them probably to this day.

My father is a brilliant man of many talents. He bought and restored a "Criss Craft Cabin Cruiser" boat, and we would go out in the ocean near San Francisco bay to fish. This would have been when I was about five or six. He baited my pole, which had a "magical" rainbow fishing line. Well, it must have been some kind of magic, for when he taught me how to cast the line, and it went into the wavy water of the bay, I got an immediate bite. I was so excited! With a little help, I got my catch into the boat. It was a seven-pound flounder, and to me it looked like a flying fish with wings. I was so proud and happy!

He instilled in us a deep love and respect for all living things, on the land and in the waters. On our birthdays, we enjoyed trips to San Francisco, where we would enjoy the many sights, smells, delicious food, and vastly interesting life along Fisherman's Wharf. Then we would go to Steinhart Aquarium, to see the many wonders there.

We got the opportunity to enjoy Stanley Kubrick's "2001: A Space Odyssey", which instilled in me a great love of science fiction. I also at one point in time got to see "The Last Question", by Isaac Asimov, at a planetarium. I was completely mesmerized when the lights dimmed, and the seats mechanically reclined!

We lived at one point at the top of Main Street in Martinez, California, in a Spanish style "adobe" with curvy red tile roof, and a large front sun window. This would have been about my tenth year of life.

He always fascinated me with his way of putting things together to accomplish his many endeavors. We had a back area, with a wooden gate. He made a stencil with cardboard of ivy leaves, and spray-painted the design on the gate. It was lovely, and we shared in his sense of accomplishment in these many "home" projects.

We had an Avocado tree in the backyard, and he helped me plant a pumpkin plant that I had germinated at school in the back area. We had the opportunity to visit many years later, and there were still large pumpkins growing in back!

One Mother's Day there, he got my mommy a very nice gift, and proceeded to hide messages and clues in a number of places, that led to the surprise. It was so much fun following this trail, and I realize was also a metaphorical learning game that I would incorporate into my CPU.

While working for Radio Shack, my dad instilled in me a wonderful interest in electronics. He would buy us fascinating electronic projects, including "100-in-one" kits, where I learned about the functions of resistors, capacitors, transistors, and many other things.

This one-hundred project kit was an ingenious device that had components that were hooked to numbered spring terminals, which were easy to connect wires to make a variety of DC circuits. I made keyboards, AM-FM radios, and other interesting things with these excellent learning toys.

He always encouraged my pursuits, and I was able to astound him with some of my projects and observations. I had a solar cell, which turns light into electricity, a portable radio, and a flashlight. I asked him if I could convert the audio signal into the light beam, and then convert it back into an audio signal. So, with his encouragement, I hooked the flashlight in series with the headphone output of the radio, and pointed it at the solar cell, which was plugged into my guitar amplifier. It worked, and I could hear the music from the radio on my amplifier! I was later to discover that this process is now used for communication through "fiber optic" cables.

He always seemed to have interesting ideas for making money, and besides working very hard all of his life (another great example to follow), he is a talented and accomplished musician. My all-time childhood hero is so proficient and professional playing the guitar that he fills in a three-piece band nicely, playing a very good combination of rhythm and lead.

The extra money that he brought in by playing gigs on the weekends really helped us make ends meet in a modestly spectacular way. On certain exciting days, we joined him at "Jam sessions" in places like Pix Patio in Concord.
There would always be a lot of food, fun, and merriment.

I admired his position as Manager when he worked. He had great people skills, and was always admired by the many interesting people in his employ. One was Ray G, who apparently had problems with alcohol. He killed himself while playing an inebriated game of "Russian Roulette". Bill Wiley was another, who helped instill a love for poetry after reciting Lewis Carrolls' "The Jabberwocky", with great zeal and gusto.

When I was twelve, two marvelous things happened: my sister Sara was born, and my father made his dreams come true. He had gotten fed up with Tandy Corporation, who owns Radio Shack, and life in California. So he got three partners to go in on a business venture, and got to fulfill one of the great dreams of his generation: to own your own business.

In the summer of 1976, we packed up and moved to Rock Springs, Wyoming. There, we took an auto-body shop in Green River, about twenty-four miles west of our new home, and converted it into "Western Audio". He made the sign for the store by hand with painstaking detail and precision which was well lit and decorated with the famous horse and rider, which is a symbol well known, and on Wyoming's license plates.

There we sold stereos for the home and the road, and other various electronic devices and components. I got to learn to install stereos and CB's, which were all the craze then, especially among "truckers", of which there were many, as we lived right on one of the main conduits of travel, I-80.

I did not care for Wyoming at first, but as time went on, I gained a tremendous love and respect for the "high desert", and for rocks and minerals. We used to go up into the hills behind our trailer park (this is after we had moved to Green River), and dig fish fossils out of the sedimentary shale. It seems the whole area was an ancient sea bed!

We moved at a time when there was great growth, wealth, and prosperity. About five years later, that all changed abruptly. The business venture went bankrupt, but will forever be etched on my mind as a wonderful time in our family's history.

My dad went on to work hard in the oil field, and then moved back to California and worked there for the State for many years. He separated from my mother when I was 18 years old, and has a loving wife, and a son and daughter from his second marriage. He moved back to Wyoming, and lives there with my step-mother. He still works full-time at the age of eighty, and plays professional music.

A very driven and artistic individual, he has sketched, painted, etched on glass bottles, and written a great deal of very good poetry, prose, and stories. You will be blessed, vastly entertained, and fortunate if you happen to get the opportunity to read his compelling writing.

We may not have been wealthy, but one of the many things that he taught me is to be able to enjoy the "finer things in life", for which you do not have to have a lot of money, but are priceless in value.

He always provided well for us, and I had a magical, fulfilling, and wonderful childhood as a direct result of his desire to provide for us; above and beyond what a lot of my friends had.

I am posting this today as an early Father's Day gift, and pray that it will be received with understanding, open mindedness, a love of good memories, and mutual respect.

Happy Father's Day!
Your Loving Son, Darren

To Be Toby, a Brilliant Boy

For my brilliant nephew, Noah

To be Toby,
a brilliant boy;
is to see
resilient joy!

To be free
to speak your mind
as you become *aligned*
with the *daily grind*

Do you find
disarray
of the kind
that makes your day
cloudy?

~Do you get dowdy?~

So many priorities,
and styles of conforming
to the choppy seas
of social swarming

~thought bubbles are forming~

So many rules
written (and otherwise)
spoken by *fools,*
in disguise

~Don't be fooled by their lies!~

What exactly did you expect
of the "entire production"?
The induction of the
*endless comparisons**

~as twins are a "pair of sons"~

Do you compare
their satisfaction
in proportion to
your own?

~Are you alone?~

Do you think
your take is fair?
Take a long drink
of the cool, clean air

~and *prepare*~

For the next scenario
Don't be *perplexed*
if it is a fiasco;
or a rodeo

Yee Haw!
Get on that bronco,
and get bucked off
onto the dusty ground

You dust yourself off,
and look around-
there's not a sound,
you have suddenly found:

~That you are *dreaming*~

And gasping from *asthma*!
Everything *seeming,*
to blend into that *miasma*
of *disarrayed data*

"What does it matta",
you think
as you blink
a sudden kink
in your link

~to *reality*~

A wrinkle in time
that induces rhyme
as you climb
the ladder to
"Success"

Full enlightenment;
(a lull, and then *the scent*)
of your environment
made of elements

The building blocks
of everything
while all of the clocks
are incessantly ticking

~giving *time* a licking~

Carbon-based
in your face
this "human race"
you can't erase the past

So, make the *last*
thing that you do: last!
If you sense disaster
in your line of sight;
becoming the master
of handling fright

As a chime
softly tinkles,
an obscure link to
that "wrinkle"

~That caught "Rip Van Winkle"~

You decide that,
if you *can't hide*,
that you would like to ride
away on the wings of escape!

~sometimes you gape~

In whatever *shape*
they might take, but
make no mistake:
that to *truly* do so,

~You first must die~

Yet, you continue to ask why?

(Humming) Birdbrain

the beak of a bird

pierced my skull into my brain

I started humming

Last Supper

the praying mantis

laying in wait, late Autumn

for his last supper

My Camouflaged Friend

my friend, Gillian

reptilian in nature

a chameleon

The Lonely Light

Solitary flame

abounding **dark** surrounding

bravely, burns *brightly*

Newton the Newt

I have a good newt

he appears to be a mute

but he is quite cute!

Eyes Wide Open

open *wide* your eyes

look at where you are going;

mindful of the *past*

A Shift in the Wind (Ida's Tears)

"I am a being of Heaven and Earth, of thunder and lightning, of rain and wind, of the galaxies" Eden Ahbez, musician

What goes up, must come down.
But sometimes it just hangs around
up there, in the air-

Causing speculation
in the relation
of exactly
~where~
it is going; the
Wind Shift blowing-

At times, out of proportion.
Exactly which is your portion?
How is it connected?
Where is the energy octopus directed?

Its tentative tentacles
reaching, teaching, leaching
our delicate desires;

having been formed in the
formidable fires
of the primordial past.

~W*hat*~

about the fact that nothing lasts?
But the past
has been intrinsically woven into
an infinitely finite point in time.
A wrinkly rhyme that leads to a

~why/when~

vector, an
erstwhile energy connector
that spirals into precisely

~how~

to resurrect the cause and effect;
in a mysterious manner that redirects
those elusive, effusive octopi appendages-

Which are inherently wrapping around
that which I have found:
a gleaming grain of truth

Once the Shift Wind has
blown away the chaff,
in a way that makes me laugh;
otherwise I'da cried-

On that wide, wide

~plateau~

where those fleeting, floating
thought-bubbles reside

ʘ ʘ ʘ ʘ ʘ

Ravenous Planet

swallowed by the earth

previous chapter: ending

finally I'm free!

Smallest Fish in the World

the tiniest fish:

exactly which one is that?

the microfiche

Snowchroma

crystalline snowflake

so many pretty facets

refracting rainbows

Sparkling Air duet

when it's very cold
and there's a bit of moisture

the air is sparkling

sunlight shining through

slivers of silver mirrors

reflecting rainbows

To Reach the Masses

if you want your voice

to be heard by *the masses,*

try writing a book

My Education, Accomplishments and Jobs

Chapter X

I attended elementary school in Concord, California from 1969-1974. Kindergarten included Cambridge and Ayers Elementary schools. At this age, I remember that we were ALL friends, and Holidays like Valentine's day brought a lot of joy and excitement, as we carefully signed Valentine cards for all of our classmates.

My 1st grade teacher was Mrs. Hull; 2nd, Mrs. Hedges, 3rd, Mrs. Fenty, 4th, Mrs. Munger, who played the piano very well while we sang such songs as "Oh, Susanna", and "On Top of Spaghetti", which is a very humorous version sung to the tune of "on Top of Old Smoky".

One day in her class, some nice Japanese ladies came and told us about their culture. We learned to say hello in their language, which was pronounced like: "ohio". This would be at El Monte Elementary school. In 5th grade I had Mrs. Stanton, and sixth grade introduced me to my first male teacher, Mr. Milam. He was very straightforward, and as I recall, a very good teacher and mentor who put a lot of emphasis on enthusiasm.

I took an immediate love and aptitude to reading and I devoured books. Some of my first and most memorable ones included an Illustrated Children's bible, "James and the Giant Peach", by Roald Dahl, and a children's collection of Aesop's Fables and classic fairy-tales and other popular stories, like "The Ugly Duckling".

In the bible, I fell in love with the story of Joseph, Israel's twelfth son, his coat of many colors, and his success in Egypt, after being sold into slavery by his brothers.

I was captivated reading about how he, through The Lord, interpreted the baker, cupbearer, and Pharaoh's dreams.

I attended the seventh grade at Loma Vista Junior High, in Concord, CA. One of my favorite memories is of my science teacher, Mr. Johnson. He did very interesting things, and was really good at sparking our interest in the sciences. For our final project, we combined sulfur, carbon, and saltpeter (potassium nitrate) to make gunpowder. Then we made "bombs" of folded paper triangles, and water-proof fuses. It was great fun to see whose was the loudest.

In 1976 we moved to Wyoming, and I attended eighth grade in Green River at Monroe Middle School. There I enjoyed joining in track and swimming. I also started attending Tae Kwon Do classes, which I enjoyed for three and a half years. At one point in time I attended a tournament, where I placed second place in the Kata and sparring events.

As I entered High School, I was noticing that we broke into sub-groups, or "cliques". There were the Jocks, the Nerds, the Cowboys, and the Stoners. Ironically enough, some of these "karasses" (see "Cat's Cradle", by Curt Vonnegut) overlapped, and a few individuals actually fit into all four.

In High School, I studied English, math; up to algebra II, history, and computer programming. We utilized Apple II E and II C computers with color graphics. They were new, then! I learned how to write programs with BASIC, or Beginners's All purpose Symbolic Instructional Code. I wrote a really neat program that drew symmetrical designs in the four quadrants of the screen, utilizing a random mode for direction, length, and color.

In addition to swimming and track, I was very athletic, and enjoyed many other forms of fun exercise. These included hacky-sack, Frisbee, disc golf, and bicycling. I swam a 200 meter freestyle exhibition exhibit, and ran the 200 yard dash.

At the age of seventeen I was still quite short of required credits to graduate, so I decided to take the "General Education Diploma" test, and passed with flying colors. I scored 98% in the science section, missing only two of one-hundred questions.

Then I went back to continuation school, and earned my High School Diploma at the age of twenty-two.

In all of this, I began to develop, learn, and cultivate an idea of how "all of this" fits together. I wondered, what motivates people to do the things that they do? Why do some kids become "stoners", while another very similar individual maintains a 4.0 grade point average?

I noticed at an early age that my friends would take me aside and talk about problems that they were having. I guess they intuitively "knew" that I am a healer, and that I would not only be a good listener, but would usually have good constructive, positive advice to offer.

My first job was at a land-fill in Carson City, Nevada in 1978. I was fifteen, and we recycled, cleaned discarded brick, and other things. I was very happy to be working, and getting paid cash money, "under the table". I lived in Wyoming at the time, but had gone to Nevada to visit my aunt and uncle. This was my second summer there, the previous was the best summer of my child-hood. I helped my uncle George Thompson at Diamond Valley Ranch. I learned how to ride horses, with and without a saddle.

My next job was a Village Inn Pancake House, in Rock Springs, Wyoming. There, I learned how to hustle on a busy breakfast wheel, to pan-flip eggs, and to separate them to make the best pancake batter. My boss, Dennis, gave me some great advice. He told me that it was a good idea to maintain an attitude of professionalism on the job, but included that it is a good policy to adopt to life, in general. That advice was invaluable, and I adopt it to this day.

I had a lot of jobs after that, which included: Cooking doughnuts (it took me years before I could enjoy them again!), pouring and finishing cement, roofing, landscaping, and painting. At one point I was an electrician's apprentice for the School District. I have canvassed for the National Toxics Campaign, and most previously, I helped open the IHOP in Yuba City, California. This would have been around 1998.

In addition, I have played professional music since the age of sixteen, and still practice every day. When I perform in Sacramento, I usually make ten to twenty dollars an hour. The most I ever made was playing on Amtrak, and around the bars, when smoking was no longer allowed.

I also do beadwork; I make, sell, and give gifts of my bead projects. I have learned to utilize stones, gems, and minerals into my work. One of my trade-marks is a braided design, with three stones in the middle of the braids.

I currently work for an independent polling firm, conducting public opinion surveys. I love learning how to maintain a professional attitude on the phone, and I have gotten very good. My percentage of quota went from 87% to 110% to over 140%. It fluctuates, but is currently at 113%. It is necessary to pay attention to detail, to read verbatim and remain up-beat and cheerful, no matter what!

My greatest achievement of this period in my life was overcoming a twenty-four year addiction to methamphetamine. I learned a lot, and I am able to utilize my message of strength and hope with other suffering addicts. My message is loud, clear, and quite genuine, as I talk from a position of knowledge. I have been clean since February 4, 2016.

I would like to once again express my sincere appreciation for the help that was provided by my Uncle A.J., who gave me moral support, spiritual guidance, and firewood, and my Aunt Emily, for her generosity, advice, and transportation after my hernia surgery. Thanks again!

Not Fake Cake

"Be who you are and say what you want, for those who mind don't matter, and those who matter don't mind" Dr. Seuss
For my Aunt Emily

My flesh had a craving
for something "sweet";
for myself, I was paving
the road to a treat.

Desiring something tasty,
I just couldn't wait!
"But I shan't be hasty",
I said *too late-*

The road led to
a worldly store.
So much to see and do,
inside, there was more!

I saw a cake
that looked decadent~
It was topped with a snake,
which seemed relevant.

I paid a dear price,
then had it wrapped.
It looked *so nice,*
my anticipation was rapt!

But when I chose
to enjoy its flavor,
my gorge rose,
it could not be savored;

~for it was a fake cake!~

So I learned to wait,
and developed style.
It was not too late,
to wait for a while-

Then I learned
after many tries,
impatience, I spurned,
as I earned a surprise!

~I was learning to be genuine~

You *can* have your cake
and eat it too!
If you are not fake,
and your heart is true.

When you weave resources,
and it turns out good;
at work are forces:
that knew it would.

Overcoming these things,
improves your strength.
Then, your heart sings,
and to your life, adds length!

Start with the proper batter,
then get some berries, black;
mix in some cream-cheese matter,
in this, you must not slack!

The "batter" is the catalyst,
that helps us

rise to the occasion-

in this, you must persist,
to *balance* the equation.

When you
put your heart and soul,
into this situation:
"You" are the starring role,
and have a *direct relation*

to the outcome-
so how come
it turned out good?

One reason is,
because you are thrifty,
and your style is nifty
so, you confidently *knew*
it would!

Through trial and error,
we gain confidence.
It is not fairer "there",
so don't straddle the fence!

If you feel
that you just can't take it,
don't fake it,
just bake it!

Try not to get too annoyed,
with so much at stake
avoid *the snake*,
just relax, and enjoy!

The Icing in the Cake

Chapter XI

As I stated in a previous chapter, I have been living in Del Paso Heights, a suburb of Sacramento, California since March of 2016. The owners of the property, known as "Northside Recovery", Bill and Patty B, have been helping people for over twenty-five years now, and they are ready to retire. So, they put the whole lot up for sale: consisting of about one-half acre, with seven dwellings. The biggest is the main house, where I lived. The other quarters are the owners' house, two of the managers who live on grounds, and five two-bedroom cottages. These are for people who put in their time, and earn this spacious privilege. At one point in time, I was going to move into a cottage, but it turned out to not happen, due to a conflict of personalities.

Well, Bill and Patty got very excited, because after only being on the market for about three months, they found a buyer. We were given two-week notice to find another place to live. Bill G, the main manager, really went out of his way to get us all places to live, except for the ones who chose to go to the streets. He found me a room in a large, spacious house about ten miles north of Northside Recovery. It is owned by a very gracious hostess, Diane, who is also in recovery. She resides there with her father, Ted, who had suffered a stroke. He was doing quite well, in spite of that, at seventy-nine years old. Jimmy also lives there, a very nice and helpful young gentleman. The last resident was Michael, another older gentleman. I paid the same amount on rent, $550.00 a month, but here it included food.

It was a very quiet and peaceful place, next to the Chapel Chimes Cemetery. A male buff-colored Cocker Spaniel and four roosters completed the count, with the latter gleefully announcing the rising of the sun every day.

I have been working a lot, and the biggest problem was that I lived so far from a bus or train stop. So, in order to plan wisely, it was necessary for me to get up three hours before work.

Then, something unexpected happened: the deal fell through, and Northside did not get sold. Bill G. called me, and told me that there was an opening in a two-bedroom cottage. I accepted, and moved in on June 29th. Now, not only do I have my own room, but it is in a lovely cottage situated amidst a gated courtyard. There are four other cottages, and then the owner's house, and Bill G's house. And my good friend Curt is my room-mate again!

There are laundry facilities, a lush green lawn, roses, and a hammock. It is very peaceful and quiet. I like to sit out front in the morning and enjoy my coffee as I practice my classical music.

I have my music, my writing, and an extensive bead kit. I am more content than I have ever been, and I have sufficient money to cook nice meals, and pursue all of my hobbies, one of which is cooking. So, I am including with this chapter one of my own signature recipes that I have developed.

I know that The Good Lord works in strange and mysterious ways. When I entered recovery, and started giving everything to him, and being thankful for ALL that He has done in my life, I am rewarded with even more. Romans 8:28 states, "And we know that ALL things work to the good for those who love God, to those who are *called* for His purpose" Furthermore, I will claim Proverbs 3:5-"Trust The Lord thy God in *all thy ways*, and lean not unto thy own understanding; 6-Acknowledge Him in all thy ways, and He will direct thy paths". He has blessed me immeasurably, and I am very grateful.

Blackberry Chess Cake

1 yellow or butter cake mix, 1 package room-temp cream cheese, 1 16oz. can Mandarin orange segments, 3 c fresh or frozen blackberries (or fruit of your preference. I originally used cherries)

Prepare mix as directed, but separate the eggs first, and beat the egg whites to a firm peak, as if making meringue. Then fold into the cake mixture, after beating in the cream cheese.

Place in a pan coated with shortening and flour; then put berries and mandarin segments on top. They will settle as the dessert bakes. The thinner the better, as thick cakes of this type do not cook well in the middle. If the cooking time is 40 minutes, check then, and every ten minutes, as this mixture takes longer to solidify.

Icing:

1/2 cup unsalted butter, softened, 1package (8 oz.) cream cheese, softened, 1teaspoon vanilla, 3 cups powdered sugar, plus more as needed, 2 tbsp. blackberry juice.

1. In large bowl, beat softened butter and cream cheese with electric mixer on medium speed 2 to 3 minutes, scraping bowl occasionally, until smooth and creamy.

2. Stir in vanilla and berry juice, then stir in powdered sugar. Add more powdered sugar as needed until frosting is a thick spreadable consistency.

Let cake cool before frosting.

The Legacy of Shelly's Gems

"Hark, now hear the sailors cry. Smell the sea and feel the sky
Let your soul and spirit fly into the mystic" Van Morrison
~For Shelly~

A rainbow of brilliant shades
refracted in their radiance.
By heat and pressure, they are made,
and the colors conveyed, gradient.

So lovely to admire,
colors mirrored in your eyes.
Reflecting your desire;
shaping truths out of lies.

My friend, Shelly, a confidant,
collected these shiny gems.
It was more than I could ever want,
when she gave me *all of them!*

I thought the gift extravagant,
so I made her some specialties
that were simple, and elegant;
for her and her family.

The legacy of Shelly's Gems
lives on from Del Paso Heights.
They are a lasting emblem
of all that is *good* and *right.*

Then the day turned into night
and the darkness descended.
These colors, removed from our sight;
but their brilliance was not ended-

Their vibrations weave into the dark,
and have a mysterious way-
just the tiniest spark
reveals a touch of gray.

A "Mystic Topaz", was the first
that I fashioned into a pin.
Alas, it was lost, in a blinding thirst!
"Into the mystic", it re-surfaced again.

It seems that these "treasures"
have a mind of their own;
that cannot be measured
by any mere mortal, alone.

The delicate matrices are connected
by gossamer energy lines.
Into the magnetic field: directed,
as they lay in wait in secret mines.

With Amethyst, and Citrine too,
so many shapes and sizes.
Opals, Quartz, and Sapphire Blue,
a wealth of shimmering surprises!

Although our lives are fleeting,
these beauties last a bit longer.
And as we are meeting and greeting,
our affections are growing stronger.

Our flesh will decay and rust,
but memories live on forever.
For, we are all made of *star dust*,
flowing into life's river.

As these jewels filter onto the earth,
their legacy connected to ours,
as one passes, this gives rebirth
to the gentle showers.

That produces the Royal Rainbow;
which reveals the seven hues.
A promise, and a lovely show-
which restores and renews~

A cycle, endless in nature
of conflict, flux, and change.
A logical nomenclature,
to twist, shift, and rearrange.

Much like the double-helix strand
of our genetic map: DNA
As ever; united we stand
bold, alive, and strong today.

When you see a "sparkle" in my eyes
and a bright presentation,
do not be too surprised,
with the overall situation;

If I give you a shiny present,
hold it close to your belly-
it will make your day more pleasant;
thank God, then me, then Shelly!

I feel that I've scribed these words *before,*
in another time and place . . .
according to *humanities' lore*,
nothing can be completely erased.

So, consider the variety
of these shades in all that you do-
As we form, and join
The Society
of Elegant Déjà Vu!

Where I live at the backside of Northside Recovery, I have a friend and neighbor named Shelly. As we got acquainted, she found out that I made jewelry and beadwork, and that I utilized gems and minerals. She had collected an impressive collection, but had no further use for them, so she gave them all to me. There must be close to fifty+ gems!

It was difficult for me to accept such a gift, but I understood that there was a deeper meaning behind it. So, to honor her and this wonderful gift, I made some jewelry for her, her son and daughter-in-law, and her grandchildren, and I gave her a wonderful book about gems that has color illustrations, and the healing properties of all of these minerals. I have been learning to mount stones. I have made three tie-clips, two with opals, and one with a gorgeous purple-red Garnet. This was a birthday present for my friend Mike, whose Birthday is in July; so a Garnet was the closest that I could come to July's birth-stone, which is a Ruby. I am also learning to be more responsible with these valuable items, as I have already lost one Mystic Topaz, and two opals. But, in the grand scheme of things, I think that they are going on to benefit whoever found them, and therefore fulfilling that "deeper" destiny to which I am hinting at in the poem.

Brother Badger July 26, 2017

My Dream Shelf

"Flying dreams mean that you're doing the right thing with your life"
Douglas Coupland. Thanks to Trisha, aka bucketlist, for her input.

On an odd end note,
I think I would like to float-
way up among the fluffy clouds
where the noises aren't uh, loud.

Up, up into earth's atmosphere
where the air is pure and clear.
'What' and 'where' are not a fear;
is your life's cloud floating near?

Gliding on the trusty trade-winds,
to see where they might begin.
Then I'll turn and fly upside-down
to look and see what is around-

the outside of our airy layer.
I'll close my eyes and say a prayer-
I'll ask for things,
that the future might bring.

I know I'll find them, in my quest-
but it's not quite clear,
how they will *manifest*-

~The wheel is still in spin,
so I will turn again~

To go back into myself-
put this dream upon its shelf;
and then, in my own poetic way,
get ready for a bright new day!